John D Slater

The Norfolk Miller's Daughter

Bijou Productions

Published in Great Britian in 2017

Bijou Productions,

Apt4 – 3 Sands Lane, Bridlington, East Riding Of Yorkshire, YO15 2JG

Copyright © John D Slater 2017

ISBN 978-0-9549614-3-5

Acknowledgements

"Sir James Reckitt – A Memoir" - Desmond Chapman – Houston – published by Faber & Gwyer 1927.

The Smell Of The Continent: The British Discover Europe
By James Munson, Richard Mullen – Pan Books

The History Of Reckitt & Sons Ltd – Basil Reckitt
Anne Reckitt's Diary – Basil Reckitt
History, topography and directory of the town of Nottingham, printed & published 1834 by W. Dearden
Wikipedia for a great deal of background

Preface

Up to the year 2014 few people in The British Isles - and others world wide, would have not been able to go to their medicine cabinet, the cupboard under the kitchen sink, or to a shelf in the utility room and not find at least one product bearing, somewhere on the label, the name Reckitt. Amongst many others, it could be Dettol, Harpic, Gaviscon, Cilit-Bang, Calgon, Finish, Strepsils, Nurofen, Airwick and now Scholl products.

From 1840 - to 1938 the company was known as Isaac Reckitt and Sons, and then simply Reckitt and Sons. From 1938 - to 1999 it would have been Reckitt & Colman and from 1999 to 2014 Reckitt Benckiser.

Alas, from 2014, the name Reckitt disappears from the label and the company has simply become RB; though now probably one of the biggest domestic and pharmaceutical product manufacturers in Europe - and throughout the world.

But if it hadn't been for a miller's daughter from Norfolk, it's probable that, none of it would have happened.

She was born Ann Colby in 1798 – met Isaac Reckit in 1817 and became Ann Reckitt in 1818. From then on she was to be Isaac's strength and stay, upholding not only him, in all aspects of the ups and downs of his life but her son's and daughters as well.

Ann was described by her son Sir James Reckitt as a

wife in ten thousand. He also referred to her as a heroine.

From their humble beginnings she had a practical interest in the well-being of their workers; at one time even taking classes in reading and writing for employees who lacked the basic skills. Few families from the Hull area would not have, at some point in time, at least one member of their family involved in the manufacture of Reckitt products; to have a job with Reckitts was thought to be quite something and Reckiits treated their workers very well.

Sir James Reckitt was said to have announced to the board one day that he considered it a poor show, that when they lived in quality houses, their workers lived in comparative squalor; and so came into being Hull's Garden Village - decent housing for their workers. It is still today one of the prides of Hull.

In 2001 the author met Isaac & Ann's great grandson, Basil Reckitt - then aged 96, whose books, kindly loaned to the author, have revealed much about his great grandparents; though much had been written about the company and its growth, it was from this meeting that the seed of an idea was planted to tell Ann's story.

At that time the author was living in a house on the banks of one of Lincolnshire's many waterways; a little further along that waterway, known as The Maude Foster, was a windmill - still in operation producing flour to this day; it was one of Isaac Reckitt's early endeavours. Isaac and Ann were to spend the first 11 years of their married life in Boston, place of the mill and where the first four of their children would have been born.

It's a long way from the French Riviera town of Menton, the place where our story opens and where Ann and Isaac's son has been taken to see if he can be cured of the dreaded disease consumption, which eventually came to be known as tuberculosis.

The year is 1862 and Ann has just had the news delivered to her by telegram, that her beloved husband Isaac, who had previously been with them at Menton but returned to Hull, subseqeuntly becoming ill and has died.

Much of the research for this book has been gleaned from a journal which Ann kept whilst they were staying on the Riviera; some of the words in the story being taken directly from her own writings. Other material has been gleaned from visiting the various locations.

Where the facts have been available, they have been used but the colouring of the story and filling the gaps are from the imaginings of the author.

Thanks for help go to Dr.Roger Rolls – for information on the history of Bath Hospital and mineral water treatments; Gordon Stephenson (Reckitt Archives) for help with research. Basil Reckitt and his wife Mary for loan of books and background. Ruth Whatley and Carole A Holmes for moral support and acting as proof-readers.

"For my darling daughter Philippa ,who always thought that her daddy could do anything."

Chapter one

"Isaac Reckitt – you are the stubbornest of men! Don't you realise how badly you're getting? Soon you won't be fit for work at all – then what will we do?"

Ann smiled to herself as she recalled these words of over thirty years ago; such a thing to say to a husband of not yet ten of them; how bold. But he needed telling. Those memories drifted by her as she sat looking out of the window; their bedroom window, the one that Isaac should be sharing with her at this moment; the one with the stunning view of the bay. For views, apart from the resident's lounge, they possessed the best room in the Menton pension; booked for the winter period and right up to the end of May.

As she sat there alone, Ann wondered whatever made that particular day in her life come to mind at this moment. Though her face smiled at the recollection, her heart bore no smile; she scanned the telegram in her lap for the umpteenth time. Three days hadn't passed, since the devastating missive arrived; she still found the words hard to take in.

"Father passed away peacefully..............."

Peacefully? Isaac – a peace loving man?

Yes – of course, thought Ann, he was a peace loving man, though at times he could be anything but peaceful. When he got something in his head that he wanted to do there would be no deterring him. The thing must be done at once. Like his decision to go back home – instead of remaining in this delightful place for the duration of their vacation. If only he'd stayed with them, enjoying the mild health giving climate and not burdened himself with the thousand mile journey back to Hull; and a cold and damp Hull it would have been.

But he needed to keep an eye on the business; but why – when three capable sons kept everything going? Isaac Reckitt & Sons. Partners all – certainly but Isaac still wanted to have his own say in things. That was Isaac – wasn't it?

If only! If only! She smiled again to herself as she recalled what her gran would have said. "If we took all the 'if onlys' of life and put them into a line – t'would stretch from John O'Groats to Land's End – and back again!" Grandma Kinsey was full of wise sayings.

Her thoughts drifted back again to that day in the little house in Boston – their first home. The day when, whilst kneading the bread dough on the scrubbed kitchen table, Isaac was to be given her piece. He was to be told what she thought and he must listen. With hands on hips – her mind made up – she looked across the room at him; her dear, infuriating at times, Isaac; his nose buried as usual in the windmill business account books.

He lay on the settle to the side of the kitchen fire, propped up on a pillow, rested against the dresser; the best position to be in without lying flat; warmth from the kitchen fire eased his rheumatic pain, though never taking it away completely.

How she loved this man, though at times she found his stubbornness a trial; action was needed and soon, or he might never work again. Ann never lost sight of the fact that the mill meant a lot to him. But he must appreciate that his family needed consideration as well; there's nothing for it determined Ann – I must force the issue.

"Isaac, have you not heard a word I said?"

Isaac briefly looked up from his accounts books, smiled at her, "Of course I heard dearest wife – every syllable. And I love you the more for your concern but summer will soon be here and all will be well!" He smiled once more and went back to his accounts.

Ann seized the bread dough and slammed it onto the table with such force that the milk jug, bowl, and rolling pin danced a jig. At once, Isaac the desired result being achieved, gave her his full attention;

"Ann – I've never known you like this before. "She put the bread dough back into the big earthenware bowl covering it with a damp cloth and then wiping her hands on a kitchen rag, she came over to the settle to stand by him. Anne's face bore a look of exasperation and she shook her head, "No Isaac you haven't known me like this before and I'm much pained to come at you in this way but . . . ." He looked up at her - "But what Ann?" Ann laid a hand on his shoulder.

"But what is a wife for, if not to make husband and children her first concern?"

Isaac put the account books down on the dresser.

"Never doubted dear wife."

Ann drew out one of the fiddle-back kitchen chairs from

under the table and brought it over to sit by him.

"I hope it's never doubted Isaac, but I do urge you to give the matter some serious thought."

Isaac took her hand in his and smiled at her.

"Could a man wish for a better wife? I count myself fortunate indeed you chose me for a husband."

She smiled at him warmly, knowing this not be flattery; Isaac wasn't given that way.

"And I count myself fortunate in having you for a husband." Isaac gave her a friendly dig, "Surely not this stubborn, pig headed fellow!"

Laughing, she flicked him across the ear with the kitchen rag, "I never called you pig headed."

He joined in the laughter, "No – perhaps not – but you thought it!" They both laughed together; it was an easy laugh – though potentially a tense situation. Isaac's drollery was at times a tonic; he was never happier than when given an audience for his mirth. Isaac wrapped his arms around her waist and drew her to him and she rested her head on his shoulder. They remained close for a few moments longer, simply gazing at the flickering of the kitchen fire. Isaac spoke first.

"Ann – you didn't get much of a bargain when you got me – did you?"

"I got the man I wanted – that's all that matters!"

"But what about your sisters – they've done well for themselves – haven't they?"

"They married the men they wanted – I married the man I wanted you."

4

Isaac gave a grunt, "Yes – and look at us; we struggle from day to day."

"We're better off than many."

"Yes – we are – but your brothers-in-law hold good positions in society; highly respected in their own realms. And what's more they can ...."

Ann butted in. "And – Isaac Reckitt – some day, you will be highly respected in your realm; and you'll take your position in society; a position equal, if not higher, than my brothers-in-law."

"If left to you, I would be ruler of the land."

"Well Isaac – why not?"

"Ann – I couldn't even manage to be a profitable corn merchant or an effective wool dealer; and as it stands at the moment, a failed miller may be my next accomplishment."

She'd lost count of the number of times Isaac accorded that himself with this self deprecation.

"But Isaac – you can't take the blame. So many factors need to be considered; high corn prices, poor harvests, shortages and the crippling Corn Laws have all but ruined countless businesses. What's more the government legislation against grain imports, meant to help farmers, is reducing the poor to starvation."

"You have a point Ann ......" But Ann, in full flow now, intended to continue – she had the "floor" and she must not miss her chance.

"What's more Isaac, the pernicious rheumatism and all the handicaps it brings to your life, is also not of your making. But what could be of your making is seeking a lasting cure."

Isaac gave her his fullest attention and thought before he spoke again. But he knew it wasn't going to be what she wanted to hear.

"Rheumatism – rheumatism – the bane of the Lincolnshire fen dwellers; there is nothing new about it and anyway, spring will soon be here – followed by summer and you'll see – your stubborn Isaac will be a new man." and giving her another hug returned to his books.

She looked at him for long moments and then shaking her head wearily, got up from the chair, walked across the kitchen, reached for her cloak and bonnet from the coat hook at the back of the door, picked up her basket and went out of the house. As she walked, the rhythm of her footsteps appeared to be saying "Isaac – Isaac – Isaac – infuriating Isaac!" Not more than twenty yards from the house, she realised she hadn't kissed him; so back she came.

Isaac, still in the same place, nose in the account books, knew why she'd returned. He smiled at her as she walked over to him to give him his kiss.

"Thank you Ann."

"Thank you Isaac."

Then giving him a playful push added, "We'll talk later."

Ann walked out of the house, closing the door quite firmly behind her she made once again for the town centre. As she came to the corner at the end of the terrace, she stopped to look back at their humble abode in St Anne's Terrace.

Life at that Boston house held so many fond memories for her as well as some troubled ones. It was their first home. The home Isaac brought her back to after their wedding at the

Kelvedon Friends Meeting House.

When the time came for them to move out of Boston almost thirty years ago, the corporation planned to demolish the property and build public offices; a great shame because it was a lovely little house; true – it was a bit of a squeeze for seven of them but they managed and it served them very well for the eleven years they lived there. The whole of St. Anne's terrace might well be no more; corporations were always wanting to change things. Progress they called it! OH yes thought Ann – what about places to live? What about progress here?

Ann experienced a deep melancholy as she pictured that first dwelling. Not the grandest house in Boston – money was short but sufficient unto their needs; a favourite Isaac expression at the time.

Ann never would deny this though she held that, despite their financial concerns, at St. Anne's Terrace they experienced many of the true riches which can only come with family happiness. Five of their much loved children, born at St. Anne's Terrace, proved a great joy to Ann and Isaac.

Elizabeth, ten at the time, called herself "the little mum" - never happier than when watching over her siblings. Being their first daughter, Isaac held a special place, and an admiration, for "Bessie" as he called her – saying she was so much like her mother.

Though they all attended school, Elizabeth would very much enjoy taking them through their lessons pretending to be teacher.

If she didn't marry, which Ann dearly hoped she would, then

she imagined that teaching would be her life, taking after grandmother Coleby – herself a teacher.

Charles – the eldest, at twelve, gave Ann most concern; such a quiet gentle chap but not robust unlike his younger brothers. Frederick and George at seven and five respectively, were on the whole, well behaved, though at times a pair of tricksters; what's more, if on their walks, they found a tree to climb – they climbed it and would squirt water at those passing underneath.

Francis, the youngest at four, delighted in finding new and interesting insects to bring into the house; not always well appreciated. His curiosity at all things around him was going to be an aspect of his personality and would remain all this life. He would become the chemist of the family and a great asset to the business.

The day of her recollections was Market Day and being Market Day, Elizabeth, took her brothers out early, first making sure they were all warmly attired for the cold day outside. They loved to be around when the travelling folk set up their tranklement bedecked stalls; market traders, it appeared to them never sold an item unless it glittered – a delight for any child. Ann was happy for them to enjoy it all.

As she walked into the market square, which wasn't more than a few minutes from where they lived; she looked round about her. Boston Market – it was quite something.

Quaker Meeting Friends who lived out of town would consider her most fortunate to be on the doorstep of this acclaimed twice weekly event; Wednesdays and Saturdays; the latter being today's offering.

Boston reckoned itself to have the finest of all markets in

8

Lincolnshire; folks travelling in from miles around flocked in droves for the twice weekly event; today – the Reckitt children being in the midst of them all.

They would meet their mother later to enjoy a Saturday treat from the hot chestnut woman. All this wonderment and but a few minutes walk from their terraced dwelling.

As Ann continued her stroll, she spotted her little flock gathered round the man selling a miracle cure. He was going at it great style as Ann came up behind them and listened in.

Clearly the Reckitt children enjoyed all this entertainment immensely. Ann reckoned he was coming in for his close; all the wonders of his amazing potion would have now been shared with the mesmerised listeners.

"Good people of Boston, I am not here today to take your money off you, but to give you the best health elixir ever known. Your doctor may frown on this little bottle – why you may ask? Well I'll tell you – it does his job for a tenth of the price!"

The assembled gathering responded to this with Lincolnshire good humour "You said it was free!" called out a chap, chewing on stick of celery; his lady friend joined in, "Yes – you said you weren't here to take our money off us."

Loud choruses now erupted - "That's right", "Shame on you" and "What a swizz" and other expressions.

Just what the medicine-man wanted mused Ann; he'll soon have them eating out of his hand. She chuckled to herself as she pictured what Isaac would say if she bought a bottle and took it home; nothing profane, that's for sure, but his reaction would be to the point.

"Hello Ann – thinking of buying a bottle?"

The voice came from behind her and turning to see the speaker, recognised one of the Quaker Friends who'd recently begun attending their meeting. She was a woman of about her own age; her attire very similar to her own, which was, in the main, plain in its style as it was usuaully with all Quaker women.

"It's Abigail – remember me. I remember you and your lovely children – they seem to be well entertained by the 'Quack'."

Ann appreciated Abigail volunteering her name – for at that moment it escaped her. Abigail and her husband came over to Boston from the west-country. He occupied a decent position with the port authority.

"Hello Abigail; I was just chuckling to myself as to what husband Isaac may say if bought him a bottle of the concoction."

"He wouldn't be pleased then?" ventured Abigail.

"He most certainly would not.

My husband has firm views on so called 'cure-alls'. Though, we are constantly hoping and praying we'll find reliable treatment for his complaint."

Abigail nodded at her "I'm sure you won't think me unkind but I have noticed your husband on occasion having difficulty taking his seat at meetings."

Ann smiled; the woman meant no harm. "Taking his seat! You ought to see him trying to get up; but you'll have noticed that as well."

Abigail was rather nonplussed at Ann's frankness and her cheeks began to colour.

"OH!" chided Ann — "please don't be abashed at my plain speaking. I am well aware of how Isaac gets noticed." Abigail smiled back at her but it wasn't a very confident smile.

"If you say so Ann — but I didn't mean to be . . . . ."

"That's alright!" Ann sniffed the air. Do you smell what I smell?"

"I smell all kinds of things Ann"

"AH but there's special fragrance in the air — hot Rosehip Cordial — now are you fond of the beverage?"
Abigail, recognising the aroma declared "OH yes!"

"Well come along then — let's partake of a glowing goblet at the refreshment stall."

The two ladies followed the direction of the aroma, Abigail chuckled to herself — "a glowing goblet"; this lady had quite a sense of humour; though when it arrived in its beaker — it did seem to glow.

Ann pointed to the notice on the stall — "Chairs and tables provided for the use of patrons only! That's us!" affirmed Ann — "Please be seated," carrying the beakers to two vacant seats. They shared a table with two elderly ladies who smiled and nodded at them. But they soon finished their drinks and left the table to Ann and Abigail. Strange as it seemed to her, Ann felt comfortable in confiding in Abigail but was rather glad there wasn't an audience.

For a few minutes they just sipped their Rosehip Cordials and watched the world go by. It was Abigail who broke the silence.

"Ann — there is something that can be done for Isaac and it is Isaac who's on your mind at the moment — isn't it."

11

"When is he ever off my mind I get so worried about him? But you were saying there's something that can be done for him – what did you mean?"

Abigail took another sip of her cordial then took a deep breath and explained to Ann her reasoning.

"As you know – we come to Boston from the West-country; a little village called Twerton a couple of miles outside Bath."

"Sounds like a location in a Grimm's Fairytale." ventured Ann.

"I expect it does." chuckled Abigail.

"Sorry Abigail – I distracted you; please go on!"

Abigail did go on; and the more she told Ann – the more absorbed she became, for it sounded like a miracle. She was extolling the virtues of Hydrotherapy treatment – being practiced in the City Of Bath, curing hundreds who suffered from a diversity of rheumatoid conditions.

"But these things cost money – and we . . . . well – you know," put in Ann. Abigail then stunned her with the biggest surprise of all; the treatment was free. Free that is to anyone coming to the city hoping to be cured. But it was not available free to the citizens of Bath – who they felt could well afford treatment if needed. Ann's brow wrinkled, "You'll forgive me Abigail – but this all sounds like The Brothers Grimm again."

"What – to go with Twerton?"

Ann put her hand on her mouth, "Whoops – there I go again." "Ann – it sounds strange but then again not so strange; well not to people who live in the West-country – especially around Bath. News doesn't travel as well West to East – as it does from North to South." Ann still held a mystified expression, so Abigail painted the full picture, explaining that since the days of the Roman invasion, Bath had become something of a watering shrine. Ann imagined it a place for the marching legions to call in at for a good wash; but, now, according to Abigail, evidently, the place was much more than that.

It appeared that the Romans knew a thing or two about water – not only for drinking and cleansing but also for its curative qualities. But it had taken a long time after the invasion for the English to catch on. Abigail propounded that the dilettantes relished the idea of bathing at The Roman Baths but mostly as a social event; both sexes enjoyed their dip together in the same pool – usually naked. At this, Ann gasped – "Would Isaac have to go in naked?"

"No!" laughed Abigail, "all that has changed now – treatments are carried out in individual tubs – in private. But the benefits are just the same – curative waters from the hot springs are piped to the hospital." Anne felt much relieved to learn that.

"Do you really think Isaac would be cured?"

"Oh – Ann – it would please me no end to say yes – but apart from the treatment much depends on nursing and care."

"I would attend to all of that – if only – if only. . ."

Ann's lip began to tremble, she looked as if she might begin crying – Abigail took hold of her hand. "Expert treatment, tender nursing care and a good helping of faith – and who knows what can happen."

"Yes indeed – who knows what can happen. Thank you so much Abigail."

"But Ann you have nothing to thank me for – I just shared a little knowledge with you."

13

"Alright then – thank you for having the knowledge to share!" They both laughed, embraced each other and went their separate ways.

Ann could barely wait to get home and relay all this information to Isaac; she was in such a rush she almost forgot the shopping and the children. She soon found them and took them for their hot chestnuts and suggested they could stay out for another hour. They would be better out of the house for a time; Ann contemplated this next session with Isaac was going to be something of a trial; in the event – she wasn't going to be wrong. After buying what items of shopping she needed she returned to the house.

Give him his due, Isaac listened attentively to all she'd learned – took in everything she had to say – then whoosh – he went up like a rocket. How could he go for treatment anywhere? What about the mill? How could he leave his brother to cope? Where were they going to get the money for the journey? What would they do with the children? On and on he went. His final outburst stemmed from the fact that his ailment had been discussed with a stranger; even though it was a member of their Quaker community, he was most put out.

They both sat there in silence – though she expected there was a lot more each of them wanted to say but just at that moment there was no more to be said. In short – she felt she'd wasted her breath – and in some ways should have realised what his reaction would be. But he was right in all he said – she could not contradict any of it. But she did feel that given the will to make the journey the obstacles he offered could be overcome. Their Quaker friends and family would certainly come forward with offers of help – both in practical and financial ways. But this was not the right time to go into all that; Isaac had spoken. He'd get better when the climate got better – and that was that. By Christmas he was walking with a stick. By Epiphany he walked with two. Lent found him being taken to the mill on a cart and by Easter – he was paralysed. Something had to be done!

Chapter two

Ann wondered at all those memories flooding back to her at this time of all times; maybe that was the way of things – such a lot had happened since those days. Things were not easy for them then; at thirty-four, she was then still quite young in experience, even though she had given birth to five children.

Looking back, she felt that that day was a turning point in their lives – well – one of them; there seemed to be so many turning points over the years but in many ways, that was a major one. Another major turning point on life's journey – a quite convoluted journey, brought them to Yorkshire and the town of Kingston Upon Hull. Lodgings at 21 Bourne Street was their first Hull residence; now with two more children making the family unit, including her and Isaac, of seven in all.

But Boston was, for her, the beginnings of her life with her beloved Isaac. As she thought back she felt she had so much to be thankful for, not the least of which being, family and Quaker friends. She wondered what had become of Abigail; they'd corresponded for a while then somehow lost touch. But of course, for several years Isaac and her hadn't seemed to be in one place for five minutes at a time. Abigail's husband, working as he did in the shipping industry, meant they too also were often on the move.

Boston's Quaker community at that time not so very large but such as it was, the members were always supportive of each other. Their original meeting house in Lincoln Lane had been closed in 1809 and the premises sold. Most of the Quaker flock then went to Spalding for their meetings. But when, a few years later, Isaac and his brother James came to Boston, them both being Quakers, roused the community into action to establish a second and subsequent meeting house at the former Unitarian building in Chapel Row. It all seemed such a long way from where she was now. If anyone had told her back in the Boston days, in the future, she a Norfolk miller's daughter, would be spending a six month vacation on the French Riviera, she would have thought them out of their minds; but here she was.

Again she looked out of the window of her bedroom; there was James walking along by the shore – her James – the youngest of her flock and very precious; but they were all precious to her – and even more so now that Isaac was no more. But praise be, their youngest son's health was so very much improved. It was a blessing and a joy to see the change in him and for this she gave thanks.

Though a great part of her wanted to be back home with the rest of her children who would, each of them, be grieving for the loss of their father without her there to comfort them and they, likewise, her. But it was a comfort to know that Elizabeth would take charge of things – as she always had with her brothers and sister. Anne decided that they would remain for a while longer for James' benefit; nothing would be served by them going back to Hull too soon in his recovery process. There was still cold weather to greet them in Yorkshire – June would be well soon enough for their return. It would have been what Isaac would have wanted her to do for James' sake; he had great hopes for James.

As she glanced through the window at James walking along the shore, her mind wandered to dearest Charles her first born. He would have benefited greatly from being here but she had lost him to consumption in 1842, when in his twenty-first year; just two years after they had moved to, what was to seem like their destiny, Kingston Upon Hull. If only they had known about Menton then and had the benefit of the knowledge they later gained. But if they had, she reminded herself, they would have not been able to afford such a vacation; nor would they have had the benefit of the railways in the 1830s to the same extent that they operate nowadays.

Menton was everything they required; Isaac in an instant loved the place, at once recognising the energising effects of the Riviera climate, considering them most beneficial. Anne too found the climate having the same effect on her; James, their son, gave all the appearances of being a different person since arriving in Menton.

Doctors back in Hull diagnosed James to be potentially consumptive, which was a condition everyone feared; especially Isaac and Ann, having lost Charles to the wasting disease. To help improve his younger brother's health, Ann and Isaac tried visits to various British locations which were known for having given every evidence for beneficial curative effects achieved for conditions such as James'. Initial travels took them to The Lake District, thinking that spending some time in the clean, pollution free air, of one of the country's most charmingly restful and verdant locations, would do the trick.

But it didn't; the climate being too damp, it worsened James' condition. Ilkley, which health seeking fashionable society flocked to, came up as another place to visit; alas nothing in the way of health benefits was to be gained from their visit to Ilkley either; a subsequent visit to Harrogate Spa was to produce similar results.

By the August of 1861, no improvement in James' health was achieved; a great concern to both Anne and Isaac. Seeking helpful information and advice from any quarter, Ann assiduously scanned the newspapers and periodicals; then wonder of wonders, she learned from an article in one of them about a book written by a Manchester doctor, its title being Menton & The Riviera As A Winter Climate; published in the August of that year. Anne, without any further delay, made a trip into the town centre, searching the various bookshops eventually acquiring a copy. On reading the book she found to her great joy that James' complaint was the main subject of the good doctor's writings; everything he said in the book, about the virtues of a stay in Menton and the proven lasting benefits to people who were experiencing James' condition, sounded so perfect – just what James needed; just what they all needed, Isaac and Ann included.

Ann, her main concern being always for the health of her loved ones, decided, after studying the book, that Menton would be their next destination. She read how people with respiratory disorders, rheumatism and associated ailments, had derived great benefits from their stay in Menton. Dr. Bennett himself found his own health improved beyond measure by simply being there. It seemed too good to be true and there was a nagging voice at the back of her mind saying to her that maybe the long journey may not bear fruit. But there was a chance and if anything, they would be out of a winter in Hull.

It would appear that many famous people from the literature and arts world, were now making the journey themselves, taking advantage of the invigorating climate and Dr. Bennett's services. Not a few newspapers carried articles relating to the manifold benefits in health enjoyed by an abundance of those distinguished public figures. There would be the inevitable social climbers making their way to Menton, as there always were when something seems to be new and ultimately fashionable; the ones who liked to see and be seen; but none of these would count Isaac Reckitt or herself to their number.

She smiled as she thought of all the preparations she needed to make before the journey could begin and Isaac also had much to do to confidently take such a long break from business; though, at sixty eight he liked to have his finger on the pulse, he was gradually going into the factory less and spending more time in his beloved garden. It was decided that an ideal time to leave for The Riviera would be November and so the first of that month saw them making their departure from a cold and wet Yorkshire. Folkestone, their first destination, being for the ferry crossing, was a tiring journey from Hull but just the first leg of a very long journey. It might have been shortened considerably if Ann would contemplate sailing from Marseilles to the Riviera. But if choices were available of how they might travel, Ann favoured the overland routes every time, even though sailing might be cheaper.

Crossing from Folkestone to Boulogne had been enough for her, suffering a great deal from seasickness; but in her usual stoic way she grins and bears it, hoping that suffering the temporary discomfort will prove to be worthwhile in the end.

Upon arriving at Menton for that first visit, they found they weren't the only ones looking for a place to stay. Evidently, the good doctor's book captured the imaginations of the many. Much of the available accommodation didn't greatly appeal to them. The places were too much in the town and the way the hotels faced was not to Ann's liking. She wanted something with a good view and a little apart from the bustle of the town. Here once again, Dr. Bennett comes to their aid; he recommends a pension recently opened by a Miss Stafford an English lady, and one of his patients. She had experienced the health benefits of the place, deciding to open an establishment and live there herself.

Pension Stafford's location was ideal to their needs and though the accommodation they secured not spacious, it would be adequate. The room provided for Isaac and Ann is furnished sufficiently with two comfortable beds, three arm-chairs, a walnut chest of drawers and a fireplace with marble mantelpiece. Two washstands and several other chairs completed the arched ceilinged room. James' bedroom is comfortable and well furnished, though in space, tiny for a growing lad; but Ann considered what they secured covered their requirements.

Though Isaac left them to take himself back to Hull in early December, his plan was to return to collect them in the Spring, to be back home in time for long awaited International

Exhibition a really grand affair taking place at London's Cromwell Road, where there would be 28,000 exhibitors, including Reckitt and Sons.

Can it really be three months since they had last been together? Her diary entry for March 6th 1862 records, "Oh what is life for me now? I found how utterly unprepared I was for this intelligence. I had so hoped against hope...." In a later entry she writes, "Here I had enjoyed much with my beloved husband and here I learned the bitter grief that I should see him no more in this world."

If only for James' sake, Isaac would have wanted them to stay on. Her son George, the eldest, had telegrammed her not to consider an immediate return journey to Hull; they wouldn't be in time for the funeral anyway. Ann felt the need to return, but she also saw the wisdom of remaining. Her capable sons, George, Francis and Frederick attending to the business. Isaac would say – "Everything is in safe hands." If only he'd truly believed that himself – he might still be here now.

*

Were ever seas so blue or skies so cloudless she remarked to herself? Boats, ever present in the bay, bobbed about like corks on the sun twinkling waves of The Mediterranean. A rich assortment of vessels wove an abundance of patterns on the shimmering surface, as they sailed in and out of the bay; fishermen's vessels, ferries and the sailboats of the tourists, all mingled together in what gave the appearance of the ground floor in a busy department store. Ann thought to herself, it wasn't difficult to tell the tourists and the fishermen's boats apart, the tourist craft being the shiny and pampered looking

22

ones but it all made a splendid picture. Although Ann delighted in the sea view, sailing was not for her.

James looked lost and forlorn and she knew how he felt; she was experiencing the same feeling of loss herself – perhaps more so; even here in this beautiful place she could not escape the hollow ache that was inside her. But, though at the moment she felt she would never be without that feeling of emptiness, she must put her loss behind her and now concentrate on getting James into a better state of health. It was good to see him enjoying his walk taking in the health giving Mediterranean climate and the sea air. His leisurely stroll along the shore now brought him to one of the many jetties which went out into the sea; he sat himself down on the stone wall and watched the fishermen unloading their catches.

Ann wondered just what was going through her son's mind; her youngest son but not her youngest child. Constance would have been two years younger than James if she had survived; she had gone to her Maker when she was only twelve years of age. Her brother Charles, the oldest of her children had died when he was twenty-three; her oldest and her youngest born, both taken from her; and now their father.

She expected that James, seated on the sea wall and looking out over the glorious and many-coloured Mediterranean, would be turning these things over in his mind. He would also be thinking about the business back in Hull and his brothers who were keeping everything going. She knew that James felt he should be pulling his weight along with them and it troubled him that his health was such a handicap. James was as keen, as were the others, for the success of the business. The company had had its ups and downs over the years, though the last ten of them had seen considerable progress; and she was aware that James wanted to be an active part of it. James was so ambitious but his health held him back; Ann fervently hoped that this would be all put behind him after his visit to Menton and indeed she could see considerable improvements already and they had not yet been here four months.

James would be back from his walk within the hour and then luncheon would be upon them; later that afternoon they would visit Mr & Mrs Moggeridge, a very interesting couple who rented the house adjoining Pension Stafford. Their house sported a most colourful and prodigious garden which Ann felt she couldn't get enough of. But first they must eat. Ann was delighted to see that the establishment afforded a liberal table, particularly at luncheon, though the breakfasts were quite basic; just eggs, bread and butter.

After luncheon they would have coffee in the sitting room in company with the other guests. For the views afforded, the sitting room, though not a very large room, proved to be one of the favourite rooms of the house. It contained an elegant French style fleur-de-lis patterned chaise longue, several settees and other comfortable chairs, all with the same fabric and pattern, provided for the use of the guests; they often gathered there after meals or in the early evening, some to play cards, some to read and others just to sit and chat about what they planned for the day; or what they had enjoyed that day or the day before.

Ann discovered, like herself, that Menton was new to most of the guests. They found their way to the resort as she, James and Isaac had done, through the reading of the Dr. J Henry Bennett book and his researches, which, it would appear, had found their way to the pages of The Lancet. It didn't appear that winter ever came to Menton; it was eternally spring and summer, and the views wherever you looked were quite breathtaking. Outside of the window, to left and right of her, rising in tiers, the white stuccoed dwellings clung tenuously to the hillside; a hillside which seemed that it might at any moment, tumble them, down onto the Mediterranean shore below. Each property, though, quite basic in construction, revealed its own individual character and a determination to outdo its neighbour; this mainly consisted of affecting the richest floral display possible; window boxes, seeming to contain every flower known to gardeners, vied with each other as did the hanging baskets dangling from any conceivable protuberance.

Gardens such as these, so different from the ones they were used to in Yorkshire, greatly appealed to her and Isaac, often taking their walks amongst them. Dear Isaac – how he'd loved his own gardens; they were a constant joy to him.

Ann looked again at the view before her; James was now walking back towards the Pension, returning for their midday meal which would be any time now. She decided to go down to meet him as he came in at the front door. "A good walk James?"

"Not very far mother – but enough to give me an appetite."

"I'm very glad to hear it. I'm not sure what Miss. Stafford is giving us today but we know from experience that there will be plenty of it."

"I sat on a wall for quite a while watching the fishermen unload their catches."

"I know, I was watching you from the window; you looked lost in thought James."

"Yes – well it's hardly surprising what with..........."

"I know my dear, you don't have to explain but we'll talk about it later. Lets eat shall we?" Anne took his arm and they walked together to the dining room.

Their conversation since they'd had the devastating news had been quite perfunctory; it was almost as if each of them didn't want to encroach on the other's grief.

All the residents at Pension Stafford had expressed their sympathy at Ann's loss; some were quite taken aback by the suddenness of it all. Even though they had known Isaac but for a short time, they had come to be quite attracted to him; as Ann was very well aware – on occasion, when the mood took him, he could be the life and soul of the party. But now it seemed that at every time one of the guests met her, in the hall or the dining room or the sitting room, they would feel the need to enquire how she was coping; there were almost three months to go before they returned to Hull and whilst she was most gratified and touched by their concern for her and her son, she felt that James should perhaps be taken to visit other parts of the Riviera; perhaps even, make a trip across to Italy and the city of Genoa which Isaac had talked much about.

After their meal they made for the residents sitting room to have their coffee; save for Mrs. Cooper and her daughter, the room was empty. The Coopers were seated in the favourite spot by the window overlooking the bay; Ann and James took their seats at the other end of the room. They would be visiting with the Moggeridges later, giving them plenty time for them to chat.

Most of their conversation consisted of Anne assuring her son that in no way must he shoulder any blame for them not being in Hull; not being there for his father. She hoped she had cleared his mind on that subject.

"I was only six when my father died but I remember little about it – except being very sad; most of my sisters were older, of course, except Jane who was two years younger than me and Kincey, our baby brother, just two years of age at the time."

It seemed impossible to James that such misfortune should befall to any family. "Poor grandma - it must have been devastating for her."

"Yes, it must have been – left a widow with seven of us and no immediate means of support; not a great prospect for any woman in 1802."

Anne was silent for a little while as the thoughts of her mother's plight went over in her mind; her gaze drifted to the large bookcase and the many volumes Miss. Stafford made available for residents. There was always an abundance of books on the shelves of their home in North Norfolk, mother having taught, was very keen on learning and education, especially for girls. After her husband died she was to go back to teaching as a means of providing financial support for the family. Ann's mother was an inspiration to them all and she found she was able to draw courage from the memory of her.

She did indeed have much tragedy in her life – Ann's father dying at the age of thirty-three, her mother remarried two years later and gave birth to another son, who, sadly, was only to survive till the age of seven.

James put down his coffee cup and looked at her – she was lost in thought; his mother – what a treasure she was.

"You look far away mother."

"I'm sorry James, my mind drifted into thoughts of long ago."

"Oh – you know – when I was a young girl with a new baby brother. In many ways, he was quite spoiled having six older sisters and being the youngest of the family."

"Like me I suppose – the youngest and spoiled."

"Oh James – you're not spoiled."

"Well when have any of my brothers or my sister been taken for a six month holiday to the Riviera?" Ann shook her head and smiled at him.

"James – it really isn't a holiday you know; we came here for the sake of your health."

"I realise that mother but now I'm feeling so much better we could go home!"

"Just like your father – always wanting to be on the go."
James chuckled - "Yes I suppose I am. But we seem to have been here for years."

"Be patient for a little while longer my dear – just for me."

"Very well mother."

"Cheer up – we're going to visit with the Moggeridges later – we might make a four for Whist."

"I thought I was meant to avoid too much excitement."
Ann smiled and shook her head; that would have been just the

thing that Isaac would have said; he really was so much like his father in many ways.

"I've been thinking James."

"What have you been thinking mother?"

"Well I've been thinking that it might be a good idea if we had a change of location; your father talked about us visiting Genoa. We could do that! What do you think?"

"I think it's a very good idea; but does it have the same health benefits as Menton?"

"Yes – it does; I had mentioned to Dr. Bennett, the possibility of making a visit there and he assures me that early Spring would be a very suitable time to experience Genoa."

"When can we go?"

"Well – in all fairness we should give Miss Stafford reasonable notice of our intentions; so maybe towards the end of the month would be a good idea."

"Fine – it will be something different to look forward to; then after that mother dear – can we go home?"

"Yes James – we can go home!" James finished the remainder of his coffee.

"What time are we going to the Moggeridges?" "I said we'll be there for tea at four."

"Alright – I'll meet you on the porch at ten to." She watched him walk briskly out of the room; such a different young man than the one who arrived here in November last year. She prayed that it would be a lasting cure. But why shouldn't it be; Isaac's visit to Bath had been; and what a journey that was. No trains then; just a horse and cart and her at the reins Isaac in the back. Boston to Bath almost three hundred miles. Folk thought she was out of her mind – well – maybe she was.

Chapter three

After James had left to write his letter – there was just Ann and Mrs. Cooper and her daughter, the two other guests, remaining in the sitting room. They motioned to her to join them but she was quite comfortable where she was and she indicated thus. They responded by giving, what Ann considered were, "knowing" smiles, the ones people invariably give with their heads inclined to one side. They more than likely thought that being so recently bereaved, she would be in need of company. If she had been a man, would they be making the same gesture? More than likely not!

In all fairness, the Cooper's were quite nice people. Mrs. Cooper was in Menton for the same reason as Ann was here with James – to get her daughter well again. She was a couple of years younger than James and a sweet natured girl. Though Ann thought that the way she dressed was somewhat over the top; but very much in fashion of the day. Far too frilly and frothy for Ann's taste but then again, she had never gone in much for frills and flounces; that wasn't the way of things with Quakers'. Isaac would say that if the dressmakers had to put so many frills upon things to make them sell, there would be less quality in the actual garment. She had to agree with him on that point; for him the garment had to be well tailored, serviceable and fit for purpose. Isaac would never countenance her wearing anything that might be termed as "cheap"; the same applied to the children. Quality was important to him and he was quite happy to pay for it – but frills and trimmings were out. As she glanced up from the book she was looking at(,) their eyes were on her again; there was pity written right across their faces. Yes – she was as grieved as she could possibly be about losing Isaac but she wasn't about to go into a decline. They'd had so very many years of happiness together and she would freely admit that she would have liked more; but when a loved one is taken from you – life must go on; and she had the God given strength to face life without him.

Why is it, wondered Ann, that people at large are inclined to think that woman equals weak? Even some other women are inclined to regard their "sisters" as the weaker of the two in a relationship. True, most women did not have a man's physical strength but Ann had known countless situations where a wife had held the family together when certain circumstances presented themselves. She herself had experienced many occasions in her relationship with Isaac, when she had found it necessary to be strong; certainly in spirit if nothing else. However, she now reminded herself, she had been called upon, at times, to be strong physically as well, especially when she undertook the Boston – Bath marathon; yes – and in many ways it had been a battle as well. But Isaac needed to be taken to Bath – to secure a cure for him or at least ease his suffering. He was paralysed and couldn't even walk – his poor body wracked with pain; if she was going to get him to Bath – why shouldn't she drive him there. All she had to do was hold the reins and call out "gee-up" and "Woah" - it was the horse that really did all the hard work. Ann chuckled to herself as she thought how bold she was at thirty-three years of age and her thoughts lingered on an image of Ann The Brave. It was almost comical to think back to that Norfolk miller's daughter of thirty three; but she was quite in command of the situation – anything she didn't know how to do – she would ask advice; God had given her a tongue and the gift of speech, which were both put to good use in her plan and the putting it into practice; and once more the comical side of it all struck her and she began chuckling again.

"Are you quite alright Mrs. Reckitt? It was Miss Cooper; Ann had quite forgotten that she wasn't alone in the sitting room.

"I'm fine Miss. Cooper thank you, do not trouble yourself – some comical thoughts just went through my mind. I hadn't realised that my chuckling was audible but I assure you that I am quite alright – it was kind of you to be concerned."

"Well if you are quite sure. Mama and I are soon to take a stroll to the chapel; would you care to join us?"

"That's most kind of you Miss. Cooper but we are invited to the Moggeridges for tea and James may need me before that; he has gone to write a letter and you can be sure he'll be wanting me to supply information."

"Well if you're sure."

"Quite sure Miss Cooper – but thank you again for the kind offer."

The Coopers now vacated the chaise longue by the window and rustled out of the sitting room, and with two more "knowing" smiles as they did so, closing the door behind them. Ann now quickly vacated her chair in the corner, made her way across the room and before anyone else came in, promptly took possession of the recently vacated chaise longue – chuckling to herself as she did so.

It was strange how Mrs. Cooper never talked about a Mr. Cooper – never referred to a husband and the daughter never mentioned her father; maybe he had died – or gone away; perhaps they just didn't want to talk about him. They were evidently well provided for, judging by the clothes they wore and although Pension Stafford wasn't the dearest place to stay in Menton – it wasn't the cheapest either.

Ann was quite glad to be left to herself for a while; she wanted to open memory's door a little wider onto the sequence of events which led up to her and Isaac making the journey to Bath. It would be a very positive thing to do; think about the things they had shared together; about their life with all its ups and downs but nevertheless a life lived in all its fullness. But first she would see if she could beg another cup of coffee, hoping that none of the other residents would find their way to the sitting room. But if they did – she hoped they wouldn't occupy the chaise longue by the window. She decided to leave her book and her spectacles there so that if someone did come in, perhaps they would take the hint.

Chapter four

"There you are Mrs. Reckitt – a pot of coffee for you; I've brought you some cream and sugar as well."

"A cup would have sufficed Miss Stafford."

On a small table by the chaise longue, Miss Stafford placed the tray, which upon it, in addition to the coffee pot, there was a cream jug, sugar bowl, and another small silver dish containing several, what looked like, shell shaped, biscuits.

"I've brought some Madeleines for you to try; they are a particular favourite with the French visitors."

Ann picked one up and examined it.

"Madeleines you say!"

"Named after Madame Madeleine Paulmier, the cook who, apparently, came up with the recipe; she was employed in the household of The Duke Of Lorraine, King Louis the fifteenth's father-in-law; legend has it that the delicacies were a particular favourite of his and so it is said, the king named them after her."

Ann took a small bite of one, "Mmm – delicious; do I detect a flavour of lemon?"

"You do indeed."

"I must beg the recipe – my boys would love them."

"But of course; I'll get it for you later – but now I'll leave you in peace."

"Thank you."

As Miss Stafford left the room she called out over her shoulder, "just leave everything there; one of the maids will pick it up later." Once left to herself Ann poured out her coffee and relaxed into the comfort of the chaise longue and nibbling on a Madeleine, allowed her mind to drift over her life. Now what year was it? James was born in 1833; at the time they were living in Nottingham; it could have been the Spring of 1831 or 1832 when they set out; more likely to be 1831 which was the year when Isaac became paralysed. Or was it before that? So many dates – so many things happened.

It was a very frightening time for her and Isaac, who for once, was prepared to listen to her suggestion that he avail himself of the treatment facilities offered in Bath. But he very definitely was not happy about her taking him there on her own; however, after much discussion and sometimes heated debate he finally agreed to her proposal.

Opinions had varied as to how long it would take them to get there; one thing was for sure – they would have to go through London. Though a cross-country route would have been shorter in terms of miles – the chances of getting lost were higher. Ann held out for them making the first part of their pilgrimage, Norfolk and Suffolk, not the most direct route, but their family's contacts in the counties and the Quaker network, would help in them finding a ready source of places where they might stay overnight. Another major consideration was a new bridge opening that year over the River Nene, which would take them from Lincolnshire into Norfolk. From Norfolk, through Suffolk, they would pick up the London road; thence taking their route via Essex where her mother lived; the house was on the London road at Kelvedon. Ann and her sisters had lived there themselves when they were younger; the family had moved there from Cley Next (To) The Sea after their father died. Once through London, the road to Bath, Ann had considered, might be much easier to follow; once in Bath she had thought it should be relatively easy to find the hospital. Abigail gave her some contacts in and around the Bath area.

With the help of her mother and her sisters, via countless correspondence, contacts were made with families, mostly Quaker, who lived on, or near, the route they would take; all of them willing to provide a night's lodging for them,

As far as their transport was concerned she had needed to find a low-loading cart which could be had on loan and a horse to pull it; the low loading aspect of it was essential so that she could get Isaac on and off without too much of a struggle. Carts used at the mill could not be spared but friends made enquiries round Boston; eventually they found one which had with it, a tarpaulin cover to keep them dry in the event of bad weather; the horse was supplied by the local brewery. Isaac had expressed some disquiet about the horse being loaned to them by the brewery, most Quakers being abstainers and against alcohol but she reminded him about his grandfather William Reckitt, the Quaker missionary, who on one of his trips to America, had stipulated the inclusion, amongst other requirements for the long voyage, a keg of rum, 12 bottles of port wine, 10 bottles of Madeira, 3 bottles of blackberry wine, a cask of cider and one of beer.

She remembered all the hustle and bustle of the packing and

preparations; uppermost on her list was making up a suitable mattress for Isaac to lie on; it would be placed on the cart in such a way, that by propping him up with pillows he would see something of the locations and countryside that they were passing through.

The day before they left for Bath she seemed to be answering the door every five minutes; people calling to give them things to take with them; people she hardly knew were knocking on the door with all manner of items; mostly being food. She had said to Isaac that they could do with another horse and cart to carry all the things folk brought them; a lot of the food they weren't able to take with them but it was put to good use by her little flock; the children were left in the care of Elizabeth who, though only eleven at the time, was very capable around the house, especially in the kitchen; in fact Isaac declared that her apple pies were better than her mother's and the boys adored her gingerbread men. She hadn't left her to cope totally on her own; Abigail and other friends and neighbours kept an eye on them. Ann recalled the night before their departure; all of her children were quite tearful at the thought of their mother and father going away; she wasn't very far off having a good cry herself – and she did when they had all gone to bed. For the umpteenth time, she had asked herself was she doing the right thing, then telling herself – yes she was; but now, when the big of departure was tomorrow, she had to admit – she was scared.

Chapter five

Ann felt someone tap her shoulder and nearly jumped out of her skin; turning quickly she discovered James standing there with a grin on his face.

"James – you startled me!"

"I've said hello to you twice mother; you seemed to be miles away."

"Quite correct – I was – miles and miles away."

"Where were you?"

"I was lost in my memories of the time when we lived in Boston thirty years ago."

"Before I was born."

"Oh yes – before you were born – but not long before you were to come into our lives."

"Want to share your memories?"

"I will happily share them but just for now I need to get the events in my head."

"And I've disturbed you – I'm sorry; I just wanted to check something with you."

"Check away."

"What was the name of that place we visited with the 17th century church?"

" We've visited a number of churches James."

"It was the one just over the Italian border."

"Ah – you mean the church of Santa Maria Maddalena the parish church of Bordighera in the Piazza del Popolo."

"Yes – that was the place; I knew you'd remember it; I'd better return to my room and pop it in my letter before I forget."

"Yes – you do that my dear and I'll travel through my memories a little further." "And then tell me all about it."

"I will – I will – shoo!"

James gave her a quick peck on the cheek and turned to go – only to turn back again.

"What was the place again?"

"Oh James – really! It was Santa Maria Maddalena the parish church of Bordighera in the Piazza del Popolo. Would you like me to write it down?"

James assured her "No it's alright – I'll remember it." and scurried out.

He really was getting so much better thought Ann – and then tried to call back to mind where she was up to on Memory Lane in her mission to get Isaac better. It was the May of that year when she drove the cart from St. Anne's Terrace into something which, though hopeful, was inclined to be unknown. She desperately wanted to see Isaac getting better.

In many ways, life had dealt him quite a number of, potentially ruinous, blows; not only his sickness had blighted the partnership with his brother James at the mill on the banks of Boston's Maude Foster Gowt; financial losses had not helped his general vitality. Poor harvests and draconian Corn Laws, supposedly introduced to discourage the importation of cheap corn from the continent by imposing high import taxes, and fixing the prices of corn in our own communities. These measures, supposedly designed to help farmers, had quite the opposite effect and took their toll on the grain associated businesses throughout the land; some got rich out of it as some always do but the poor people suffered because it put bread prices so high, they couldn't afford to buy it.

Everyone in the milling and farming community pinned their hopes on the general election of 1830 returning a Whig government for they were sure things would change, the Whigs previously being opposed to the Corn Laws. But things didn't change at all and it wasn't until 1848 that the hated laws had been repealed.

Ann had been a constant advocate for repeal and had made her feelings known quite forcefully whenever she got the opportunity. It didn't always go down well with certain sections of people she came into contact with. But the fact was that Isaac and his brother were fighting in all directions to help keep the mill going; both of them being under a great deal of stress – which hadn't helped Isaac's condition and which in turn hadn't helped the partnership relationship either. But if Isaac was to be cured of his illness, things might improve; please God they would.

They were to set off at 6am – first light but there was quite a little crowd outside the house to cheer them on their way. Ann wasn't sure she liked this or not; true she had given herself plenty of practice at driving the cart, which had increased her confidence and was on very good terms with, Dobbin, their horse – a sturdy cob but an audience to watch her setting off was just a trifle daunting. She was quite certain there were those amongst them who had come along to see her embark upon what they considered to be a disastrous exercise and were convinced she'd be back before she reached Fosdyke Bridge. In fact they were taking bets on how far she'd get. Ann confided in Isaac that she placed a bet herself; he was dead against gambling, as she was herself.

He'd said "Ann – what were you thinking about doing something like that; you know full well that gambling is a sin." She'd thought he might react in this way and she had her answer ready. "But Isaac my love – I don't see it as gambling – I see it as a vote of confidence in myself; surely that can't be wrong – and if someone wants to reward me with a hundred pounds for doing what I consider is my duty – who am I to refuse? Odds were a hundred to one that I wouldn't get there. I invested one pound – just like you invested in buying sheep to sell at market; you would want a return on your investment – so I invested one pound."

He'd chuckled then said, "Ann – you are quite amazing but I still think it's wrong."

"But – you have to admit that one hundred pounds waiting for me when we get back with you cured, will be very welcome. You're not cross with me are you?"

"Ann you're a woman in ten thousand and no – I'm not cross with you; just don't make a habit of it."

They said their goodbyes and having been assured of people's prayers, were off on the journey. Ann felt sure that God would hear them and her own, which included her asking God to forgive her for her little "flutter".

Word had got round about what they were aiming to

accomplish and as they left Boston and it's environs, many were coming out of their houses to give them a cheer and wish them good luck.

Ann had thought it was very good of them but she knew in her heart that 'luck' would have nothing to do with it; it was all in God's hands – just like the reins were in hers.

"Gee up Dobbin!"

It was a glorious day for their departure, not a cloud in the sky; Ann, settled on the driver's seat, felt a sense of elation now they were on the move. It was ten miles to Fosdyke Bridge, where they would be crossing the river Welland. All the way there they hardly encountered more than a dozen or so carts coming the other way; a few folk were walking to their work and now and again they came across herds of cows being taken in for milking and other travellers on the road but those they did called out their greetings and Ann responded. "Where ye bound?" - they nearly all of them wanted to know and when she replied with, "London!" heads wagged, eyes were blinked, chins were rubbed, hats were taken off and heads scratched; this along with sharp intakes of breath. Ann felt she'd couldn't have elicited a more flabbergasted response if she had said "Kathmandu!"

She reckoned that their astonishment at a woman driving a cart to London, would have been relayed to sundry others they met up with that day and probably the next day also; it wasn't every day they came across a woman driving a cart to London. Ann smiled to herself as she thought how much interest their adventure was creating; it would be only a matter of time before the whole of Boston and South Holland knew about it. But that was life amongst the country folk and the town's folk as well. It must have been something in the air – maybe it was Spring – albeit late Spring, which would soon give way to summer, though there were still plenty of hedgerow blossoms and Spring flowers adorning the grass verges. There were the white blossoms of bramble bushes, hawthorn and blackthorn; the pinks of early dog roses contrasting with the yellow of daffodils, the white cowslip, and the primroses abounded along with all kinds of daisies adorning the area. Emanating from the hedgerows, a veritable chorus of bird song wafted itself to their ears; the blackbirds were in very good form that morning.

The speed of travelling was pretty much dictated by the need for Isaac's comfort; in effect, it was little more than walking pace and nigh on three hours had passed before they were in sight of The River Welland and Fosdyke Bridge, which would take them across; they were making Fosdyke Bridge their first break; for their sake and the horse's. It was just coming up to nine o'clock and Ann was ready for a drink and something to eat.

When they reached the bridge, she pulled onto the grass verge, unhitched Dobbin from the shafts and led him to a grassy area which also sported a pond; food and drink – for the horse was all he wanted. God's creatures didn't ask for much in return for providing us with the undeniable service they do. Isaac was lifted off the back of the cart and laid on a blanket she placed under the shade of a horse chestnut tree which was so loaded with blossoms they almost touch the grass; Ann unpacked some of the food and a flagon of water and placed them on another blanket by the side of Isaac and sat down with him; the had both agreed that they missed so much of the beauty of the countryside, living as they did in the town.

On account of the streams, rivers and land drains, or gowts as they called them in Lincolnshire, there must be bridges to cross them; Ann considered, that the county must have more bridges per square mile than almost anywhere else in the World – including Venice, Fosdyke Bridge being one of them. A carter also having his break nearby, regaled them with the local legend, that in 1216, before the bridge was built, somewhere in the vicinity of where the bridge stood now, King John's treasure was lost in the crossing of the River Welland at low tide; it had come about when he was journeying from Norwich to Newark. The carter had dryly added, "If you fancy a bit of digging, I have a spade you can rent for five shillings an hour."

They had laughed and said that they wouldn't bother but when Isaac was cured, and they were on the way back to Boston, they might consider his offer. Ann had thought that they could all seek the king's treasure, if only she could get her beloved Isaac well.

Seated at the Menton Pension Stafford window, she recalled a serious conversation she'd had with Isaac at that point of the journey. She'd firstly asked him if he was happy continuing with the journey to Bath and Isaac had replied "Yes – of course Ann; true – it's a relatively easy answer seeing that you and Dobbin are doing all the work; I'm just lying back and enjoying the ride and the scenery; I have to admit thought, I'm glad we are taking our break."

"Is it very uncomfortable Isaac?"

"Well .... sometimes, when the cart wheels encounter a rut in the road."

"I'm doing my best to avoid them."

"I'm sure you are and I wasn't being critical you know; the ruts are a curse - but at least the road is dry which makes life kinder for Dobbin."

"But seriously Isaac are your heart and soul in with the project?"

Isaac took a few moments to consider this.

"As you know Ann – when you first mentioned the Bath treatment centre, I wasn't .... shall we say – in favour of it."

"Not in favour! Isaac you were furious and about me talking to Abigail about your ailment."

"Well yes – that I will not deny and to a certain extent I wondered if it might be just one of those so called 'miracle cures' which turn out to be nothing of the kind."

"Do you still think that?"

"Ann – I wouldn't be your infuriating pig headed Isaac if I didn't have just the very teeniest weeniest smidgen of doubt."

"Oh Isaac – believe me when I tell you that I too have had a element of misgiving about it all."

"You never said."

"No – I never said; but did have doubts all the same. But not any more – I'm totally convinced we are doing the right thing; you'll get your cure and be able to return to work at your mill and everything will be just fine."

"Yes – I'll return to work at the mill – that's if there's going to be any mill to work at."

With concern on her face Ann said, "Isaac – what do you mean?"

"What I mean dearest Ann is that, at the mill, things are very shaky at the moment."

Ann tried to be encouraging, "But you've had lean times before and you've got over them."

"Yes we have but I don't know how we're going to get over this; it's not helped with me not being able to make any real practical contribution."

"You mustn't blame yourself Isaac – you couldn't help it; you didn't ask for this awful condition."

"It isn't only that Ann – Thomas and I are seriously in debt; money has been borrowed now and it can't be paid back."

"We'll find a way Isaac; don't forget I'm going to be getting my winnings."

"Ann – you really are a wife in ten thousand."

"If you say so Isaac – if you say so; so now let's get something to eat. We have bread and cheese – some slices of ham Abigail gave us and for you specially, Elizabeth has baked you an apple pie."

"Lovely – she knows I like her apple pies; but – I'll share it with you Ann."

"Very generous of you Isaac!" The both laughed and tucked into their picnic lunch.

It was quite remarkable that she remembered so much after thirty years; some day she must write it all down. She looked at the clock in the resident's sitting room – amazing it was already three o'clock – the time had just hurtled by; James would be coming for her any time now and then they would be off to the Moggeridges. They always made a splendid tea after which she'd regale them with her reminiscences – they would be very interested; James too would learn something; she'd learned something herself; she hadn't realised there could be so much tucked away under her bonnet.

Chapter six

Ann and James enjoyed an agreeable afternoon with the Moggeridges. It was a delightful house; not big rooms but big enough for the beds and simple furniture in them. There were four bedrooms, or so she had been told; the property of a cousin of theirs whose usage requirement had got less over the years. They stayed there fairly frequently but apart from them, few other members of the family used the place. It occurred to Ann that it might be worth bearing in mind for any future visits they might make to Menton; it would afford them a little more privacy than a pension or hotel. A local couple looked after the house and also, when required, acted as cook/housekeeper and odd job man.

It would have been marvellous for her to have brought her daughter Elizabeth to stay here, suffering as she did from much the same complaint as James but not quite so severe. They could also have brought Elizabeth Ann, Constance and Henry with them – and little Ada – her newest grandchild, who was a constant worry to them all; she would have benefited so much; in fact they would all have revelled in it; it would do them all good; Ann felt she didn't see enough of her grandchildren, living as they did in Ipswich. They would love the allure of Menton; the sun and the sand, the beach and the boats and all the additional delights – including the rich and colourful pastries found in the patisseries and on the tea tables; as indeed were evident on the tea table that afternoon, especially the Genoa cake, which, that afternoon they'd enjoyed at the Moggeridge's tea, chock full of sultanas, currants, raisins, glacé cherries, almonds, candied orange peel and pine nuts.

Many of the recollections of earlier, Ann shared with them at tea table; they were by turns amused and moved by the story Ann told; it made her determined, when she got the chance to be on her own, to devote more time to further reminiscences; but not at bedtime – it would keep her awake but then again, nothing had kept her awake since they had arrived here; she'd assumed it must be something in the air. After dinner that evening, both James and Anne took to their bedrooms quite early. Ann determined, the next day, she would rise a couple of hours aforetime to resume the ramble through more of the memories she had begun.

Next day, at 6.30am found her up, dressed and seated comfortably on the sitting room chaise longue looking out of the window in order to catch the sun rise; and what a glorious sunrise it was on that particular morning – what a pity there weren't more people to witness it; oh there would be plenty of the local population experiencing it – some would have been up and about an hour before – or even earlier. Her childhood memories of sunrises came back to her; they could be pretty spectacular at the Norfolk coast as well, where she had enjoyed her early childhood. Cley Next The Sea had been their home for a short time before and after her father died.

But those sunrises every day were as much part of her

nourishment as the food she ate; she always viewed the sunrise as breakfast for the soul – and each day – there it was for free, provided by a loving God who never failed in the provision of this daily nutrition. There was something about sunrises that exhilarated her – energised her for the day ahead – engaged her in its intent to make the day a good day, in addition assuring her that she also had a sense of purpose for that new day – and mustn't waste it. As it peeped over the horizon it seemed to be saying, "Here I am – sorry I left you for a while but I have to do my job in other parts of the World as well." Then it seemed to rush into full view in no time at all, eager for us to enjoy its benefits, then at once reaching higher shelves, lingered around till it was time for it to do its work somewhere else.

*

Sutton Bridge was their next river crossing, taking them over The River Nene, which being the county border, took them from the county of Lincolnshire and into the county of Norfolk. The recently built Sutton Bridge, which took 26 miles off journeys between the two counties, quite fortuitously opened the very month they were making their own journey; news had reached them in Boston that the Bridge, almost a year in construction, was now open; the first vehicle to cross the new bridge was the Norwich to Newark stage coach. The structure proved a boon to everyone who needed to cross from one county to the other – so much so that, 20 years later, a new bridge, designed by the noted engineer Robert Stephenson, needed to be built.

From Fosdyke Bridge to Sutton Bridge took them six hours,

including taking in a break in the journey at the village of Long Sutton where, so the locals told them that, there was an occasion when the notorious outlaw Dick Turpin could have been seen to be galloping through on his famed ride from York to London; as it was a long time ago – Isaac declared that they needn't worry about him. It was just like Isaac to say something like that.

At Sutton Bridge a night's accommodation, with some people who were known to her mother, was pre-arranged for them. When Ann and Isaac arrived at their cottage they were both very relieved and grateful that they had got their first day's travelling over with. Ann tried to recall their names but it was no use – she couldn't remember. What she did remember was the wonderful welcome the couple gave them; they couldn't have been received better had they been royalty.

Isaac and the man of the house shared many interests in common, both having served apprenticeships at the trade of miller and both being interested in the politics of the day; get Isaac on politics and he could talk for hours and he usually did; and she was always ready to engage in debate with him especially when the politics of the day affected their life and other peoples, especially the poor. He would have been happy to stay there for a week; in truth, she would have been happy to have enjoyed their hospitality for more than just the night but they must be on the move; she didn't want to take any more time getting to Bath than was needed; the sooner they got there and back, they better she would like it; already she was missing her children – her little flock but she knew they'd be well cared for – Elizabeth would see to that.

They needed to be on the move early next day to reach East Lynn before dark; they would be spending the night there and crossing over the River Great Ouse the next day; no bridges this time – the ferry would take them over the water to King's Lynn; from thence they'd follow the coast to Hunstanton which was going to be one of the longest legs of the journey; from Hunstanton to Cley Next The Sea, where they would stay for a couple of days to give Dobbin a rest.

Boston and King's Lynn were very similar towns – both being ports – with the inevitable hustle and bustle of the waterfront. A most interesting town, which they both would have liked to have explored but they could not afford that luxury; once more they must be on the move.

When they had made "landfall" at Hunstanton it was nothing like the place it has become over the past 25 years; nowadays it is quite the "in" place to visit when in North Norfolk and is known as "the sea-bathing station of Hunstanton St Edmund". It has the unique qualification of being one of the very few places on the east coast where a sunset over the sea can be witnessed. This is achieved by the fact that the seafront faces west and the sunset is seen over that part of The North Sea which is called The Wash.

Once through Hunstanton, it became familiar territory to Anne and she recognised the names of most of the small hamlets they had passed through. She felt a sense of excitement as they approached Cley, it being the first time she would have been there since she had been a little girl. Up to that time Isaac had never visited Cley, so it was a delight to her to point out things to him, including the mill where her father had worked; true most of the things and places she showed him had to be viewed from the back of the cart – but he expressed a delight in it all.

He was amazed by the fact that though the place held the name Cley Next The Sea it had not been next to the sea since the last century, the once busy quay was no longer there, the area having silted up. A lot of the blame for this had been laid at the door of the local authority being unwilling to undertake the task of keeping the channels clear; others blamed a local land owner whose desire for more land had illegally instituted land reclamation which contributed to the silting up of The River Glaven; her grandmother had told her that in times gone by it had been one of England's busiest ports, ships coming in from all parts of the country and the continent bringing their cargoes of wines and spices – coal and cloth and many other commodities.

As she thought on her childhood home, she remembered being taken, quite regularly to the beach by her older sisters; a great place for flying kites and picnics and making sand castles. From that time, the seaside would always hold a curious fascination for her; being by it that is – even paddling in it but not sailing on it. It wasn't fear that caused her to disdain sea voyages; that might have been easy to understand, for she would certainly have been acquainted with vessels foundering on the sandbanks which sometimes had the tendency to shift from one place to another depending upon the tides. Her inclination towards seasickness was the main reason she disliked sailing; she wondered if it was the fact that she felt powerless in its grasp as well as the discomfort caused; not being able to do anything about it, she supposed was the main reason. It was a weakness, which in others she could tolerate but not so in herself; but the sea, nevertheless, remained a fascination for her.

She had gone to the sand dunes on the day her father had been taken from her; she found it hard to comprehend at six – that someone of only thirty three could die – when people much much older carried on living. It was a period of great sadness and distress in the house; it was at times like this that it was a comfort to be able to turn to beliefs shared with other Quaker friends and family and young as she was, those beliefs were in her. As she had looked out over the North Sea she reflected what her father had meant to her and compared it to what her father had meant to her mother; married in 1791 at the Friends Meeting House in Devonshire Square, London; thirteen years of marriage was all they had together – but her mother had told them all that it was a very fulfilling thirteen years – her mother was very brave; very much loved and very brave and courageous. She must take her mother as her example in her own loss and her own time of grief; at least she had Isaac for forty-one years – and a blessed forty-one years they were.

But the image of that little girl on the sand dunes kept coming back to her; in her mind's eye she was standing next to her; she imagined that she was reaching out her hand to take hold of the child's hand and to say to her - "Everything's going to be alright." But the more she thought about it – the more she felt that it could well be the other way round; the child was reaching out to her.

That two days at Cley Next The Sea passed all too quickly and it was soon time for them to be on their way again; next destination – Sheringham where, on the morning of the next day, the day being the Sabbath, Ann would attend Sheringham's Quaker friends meeting house for their Sabbath day worship. Isaac did not attend – it would have been impossible for him to sit for the hour – he said he would be quite happy to remain on the cart outside and still feel at one with the meeting, which was well attended. Word had got round that Ann and Isaac would be present and quite a number of the folk who had known the family, were keen to see how she had matured and catch up with the latest news.

Most of the morning was taken up with the meeting – and the news exchange; people wanted to know how her mother and sisters were faring; there were a dozen or more invites to have lunch with those of the flock who had known Ann and her family; it was very tempting to accept their kind offers but food had been provided by their hosts for them to take with them and they needed to be on their way to Mundesley; a half day's journey – and another twelve miles nearer Bath.

Mundesley was another of those Norfolk coastal villages which boasted a fine beach; it was another place which has become more popular of recent years as a place for health giving pursuits; huge numbers of people, taking a lead from King George who had taken to heart the recommendations of John Crane another doctor; a Lincolnshire man – and author of "Cursory Observations on Sea-Bathing", which Ann had read, observing how he advocated the benefits of sea air, sea bathing and even seawater drinking, as a cure for a wide variety of ailments.

The king had chosen Weymouth for his participation in the activities recommended in the book; other seaside places were quick to take advantage of the king's assertion that the benefits were quite remarkable; they were soon to be found exploiting the sea-water trends and developing their own amenities; Ann had considered the information meted out in the book as a possibility for James to take advantage of but in the event decided, on advice, that participation may well have the opposite effect.

It seemed that since the king had publicly declared that he was seeking cures for his illness, the whole nation had taken on the notion of good health. Some had no choice but to suffer the effects of the conditions in which they lived and the resultant diseases which went hand in hand with it; not being able to afford the fees charged by doctors and gin was cheaper.

Some of the others she classed as social invalids, who made it fashionable to be seen at the myriad of health resorts and spas which had sprung into life; each one having it's own doctor who would publicly proclaim with great confidence that this or that particular spa had the water to cure almost anything, including the "fashionable" illnesses; a part of her realised that some of the reputation of Bath had been built on the patronage of rich, fashionable and influential people.

But she must cling on to the hope and faith that Abigail had helped to inculcate in her, that Isaac would be cured; his was certainly no fashionable illness neither were they to be counted amongst the rich fashionable classes; nor had they any desire to be.

She suddenly chuckled to herself as the thoughts of all those years ago has passed through that young woman's mind and then the irony of the situation manifest itself to her; in 1831 she was making a journey to seek a cure for her beloved husband; then there she was thirty years later in 1861 making the pilgrimage to Menton to secure a lasting cure for her son.

Almost on cue, the breakfast gong sounded; she'd been sitting there for almost two hours and it had passed like a flash. Although she was, to a certain extent, reluctant to put the memories aside for the moment – she was happy to tuck into breakfast; such as it was! But no matter – she was ready for breakfast; all that time travel had given her quite an appetite.

Chapter seven

Arriving at the dining room, she found James already seated at their table. After exchanging pleasantries with the other guests, she joined him. He greeted her with a smile, rising to pull out a chair for her.

"Good morning mother; I wonder what variety of eggs it will be this morning; boiled, fried, poached, scrambled – maybe roasted for a change!"

"James – really – you are naughty!" she replied, gently tapping the back of his hand and smiling back at him.

"You were up and about early mother; I heard your door click."

"Yes – it was early – I wanted to see the sunrise; I didn't disturb you did I?"

"No – I was awake already; yearning for the eggs!"

Ann looked at him with great affection – how she loved this youngest son of hers; he had so many of his father's whimsies.

The eggs were boiled.

"We're invited to join the Coopers for a jolly jaunt; what do you say?"

"Where are they planning on going?"

"They weren't sure when they spoke to me; said we could all decide when the coach came; it would appear it's booked for ten o'clock."

"Would you like us to join them?"

"Yes – it might be fun."

"I think Miss. Cooper's taken something of a shine to you."

"Mother! She's only seventeen."

"She's very pretty."

"And still only seventeen."

"I wasn't much older when I was first introduced to your father."

"Did you take a shine to him then?"

"I must have done – I married him!"

And oh how she wished with all her heart that he was here now having breakfast with them; she could feel a tear forming on each eyelid; James noticed and for a while said no more.

Ann sipped her orange juice and declared that, here in Menton, the orange juice was the freshest and finest she'd ever tasted.

James suggested that they probably just popped out and picked a basket full off the trees each morning. There was no more conversation till after the coffee came.

"I'm sorry mother; I didn't think."

She just smiled at him.

As Ann was pouring a second cup, Mrs. Cooper was making her way to their table.

"Did your son mention our suggestion?"

"Yes Mrs. Cooper, he did and we would be delighted to accept your kind offer."

"OH good – my daughter will be pleased; until ten o'clock then." And inclining her head, gave each of them a beaming smile and left them to their coffee.

Their hire was a four seater landau or as the French call it – un fiacre. It was waiting for them at the front of the pension as they came out through the porch; the driver puffing on the inevitable cheroot; remaining seated, reins in his hands he raised his straw hat and indicated for them to board. After some earlier discussion in the lobby the destination decided upon was Monaco; not too far at all from Menton – a matter of about 10 miles which would take them a couple of hours at a leisurely pace.

James and Miss. Cooper were particularly interested in Monaco because of its recent constitutional changes. James informed them that under The Franco-Monegasque Treaty of 1861 it was now recognised as the sovereignty of Monaco. Previously, under the Treaty of Vienna the principality had been a protectorate of the Kingdom of Sardinia. Since last year it had become a French protectorate once more.

Until recent times things had been somewhat turbulent in that part of the world; it would seem that Menton had had its share of trouble as well.

Miss. Stamford had assured them that Monaco was quite safe to visit now and they should not miss some of its splendid architecture. Certainly the palace, constructed in the thirteenth century was worth a visit; Sainte Devote's, an 11th century votive chapel constructed in the hollow of the "Vallon des Gaumates". It was built to commemorate, in the fourth century, a little boat bearing the remains of the saint running aground at the entrance to the valley. She had been adopted as their patron saint.

A visit to Fort Antoine, an early eighteenth century fortress, would be a must for them to experience built at the tip of Le Rocher, the Rock, its military architecture, watchtower and the almost total solitude found there, combine together to give a very special and almost unique charm.

Miss Stafford also advised them that a good place for lunch would be Cafe Rosina which was just by the fortress. There was then a brief discussion as to how, for the journey to Monaco, they would seat themselves in the four-seater landau; two passengers would face to the front and two the rear. Mrs. Cooper, with much giggling suggested that "the children" might like to sit together.

Ann thought that, despite James' protestations, he was quite happy to accept a little hero worship from Miss Cooper.

The name Reckitt inspired keen interest in the people; the fame and value of their products was spreading. Many households in Great Britain used at least one of their products; starch, laundry blue and metal polish were the most popular and her sons had plans in the pipeline to increase their range.

How often had she heard the phrase - "Oh – but Mrs. Reckitt our laundry maid swears by your starch – and your magical blue bag they think of as the seventh wonder of the world; the footman would not be without your metal polish for our silver."

Ann, though quietly delighted, would respond with "Oh but it's my husband and sons who are the real brains behind everything. I don't really have anything to do with the business." But sometimes she wondered what would have been their fates if she hadn't insisted on taking Isaac to Bath and nursing him back to health and believed in and supported him when many others didn't have a good word to say about him; and though she wasn't involved in the manufacturing processes, she did take a keen interest in the welfare of their employees, even to establishing a factory school, where those who hadn't attained any literary skills, could receive coaching from Ann as teacher; this aspect of Ann was in no small way due to the influence of her own mother; a teacher to her fingertips.

There were those who thought that what she was doing was a waste of time; these mostly consisted of other manufacturers and businesses in the county. They would question what need was there to be able to read and write just to pack starch in boxes; or fill canisters with fluid. They would say that having an education wouldn't make them pack and label the containers any faster.

Ann was convinced that there was a need; no – not for the actual functions of the manufacturing processes – but from a sense of personal achievement perspective; individual self-worth could not be measured. The thinking amongst the critics was that if workers had too much education they would become disgruntled with their status in life; they would think they were in some way above mundane tasks; they may think that they were equal with the bosses and that would never do for some of the narrow thinking fraternity.

But they were, in fact, quite wrong; there couldn't have been a happier or more loyal workforce anywhere around those parts. What they would make of having the free services of a nurse and doctor on the premises; a plan to put into practice in the near future, she couldn't imagine. It would no doubt be something along the lines of "Reckitt and Sons mollycoddle their workers."

The main trouble was that the majority of the other factories were envious of Reckitt and Sons; they didn't like the way we went about things; were jealous of the ease with which we acquired our workforce, sometimes to their loss; oh yes it was well known in the town that a job with Reckitt and Sons was a job for life and it usually was but Isaac would not tolerate slackers – everyone must give of the best – including the managers and every effort was made to ensure fairness at every level.

Regrettably many of the other employers didn't see their staff as human beings but as some kind of beast of burden which could be worked until it dropped.

They were nearly in Monaco and they could see Fort Antoine rising on its promontory foundation from the sea below; it looked very high up to her and she was thinking that if it meant a climb then she might well pass on the ascent. In the event she chose a comfortable bench near the path which took tourists to the top of the fort. Her seat placed her in an ideal position to look out over the sea which was not without things to observe; she never tired of admiring the multicoloured Mediterranean and the many and varied craft it disported. Glancing up the cliff she could see James and The Coopers striding out to reach the summit; no – not for her.

The bench was comfortable – the breeze warm; the citrus scent of oranges and lemons seemed to be saying to her "Have a nap!"; and she did – she just closed her eyes and allowed herself into the arms of morphia; soon sleep had overtaken her. It was only a quite short nap but it produced a dream, in which she was fighting through a field of tremendously tall grass and not being able to see where she was going, found that she had been walking around in circles. But now she was awakened came back to the day when she and Isaac – a low loading cart and Dobbin, were heading south along the East coast of Norfolk, making their way to Great Yarmouth; and ultimately on to Bath.

Chapter eight

When Ann had lifted Isaac up onto the cart that day, readying themselves for the next leg of the journey, he had looked at her and said, "Ann dearest wife – you shouldn't have to be doing this you know."

He had used words to this effect before; it was difficult for her to respond without appearing either patronising or flippant. It must have been very hard for him to accept the fact that he had to be helped to do everything by his wife. He would have been the first one to consider that pride was one of the seven deadly sins; but it wasn't pride – it was a sense of his helplessness. Some days he was very downhearted, and it wasn't surprising. He felt that he had somehow failed her – and his children. When she had reminded him that he hadn't asked to have this ailment thrust upon him he would sometimes come at her with - "But I could have done something about it sooner instead of being so pig headed."

What's more, he was right, he could have done something about it sooner but there would be nothing served in her now telling him that she agreed with him. What else could she do? That day, when she had got him settled onto the mattress and wrapped a blanket round him, she stroked his newly shaved face; yes she had done that for him as well.

"Isaac – it seems so little that I am doing for you. But what little I am doing is for selfish motives as well; so I can have you back again; so we can all have you back again." He shook his head and looked away from her; she must try to keep his spirits up. As she took her place on the driving board she called behind her,

"Next destination Great Yarmouth sir; visiting the much acclaimed Nelson's Monument; reaching one hundred and forty four feet into the sky; only two hundred and seventeen steps to climb to the top."

Isaac had called back to her, "I think we'll give it a miss this time driver; but one day – you'll see – I'll run up those steps." Her eyes had filled and for a moment she didn't reply to him straight away because she knew her voice would be shaky.

She quipped "Very good sir; as long as you don't expect me to run up those steps with you!"

His laughter was his answer and she was aware that a sensitive and delicate moment had been avoided.

But he had been true to his word; he had made the ascent some ten years later when they had been visiting his cousins in Woodbridge. It would be over twenty years later that London had erected its own famous tribute to Nelson. When they had gone to see the London column Isaac was quick to point out to bystanders, that he had climbed the original column in Great Yarmouth.

One of her plans had been to take a route via Norwich which would have carried them further inland but she was more familiar with the coast roads and besides, it was easier this way to get on the London Road from Woodbridge and thence to Kelvedon.

Great Yarmouth to Woodbridge was too far for them to make the drive in one day; and Dobbin, though used to hard work pulling carts loaded with beer barrels, had his own leisurely pace.

They spent that night at Kessingland. When she had settled Isaac in bed she had gone along to the kitchen to chat for a while with their hosts; one of them handed her a mug of cocoa. Names – names – she just could not bring to mind their names but they were very kind people; Quakers – as were almost all the people who gave them lodgings on their journey.

Her mind had not been on the conversation but on what Isaac had said earlier that day; "You shouldn't have to be doing this."

She was thirty-three – Isaac was four years older; they were no age to be facing what she knew in her heart was a crisis. Supposing the acclaimed hot spring mineral water baths didn't do their stuff; didn't restore Isaac to good health. What then?

Ann came out of her abstraction as the couple were saying goodnight to her and making a request for her to snuff the candle when she turned in for the night. It was quite warm in the kitchen and she needed to take some air. The door from the kitchen, which was at the back of the cottage, led out to a long garden. She could walk out into the garden and listen to the gentle sounds of the evening; shushing waves lapping up onto the sandy beach; it was so very peaceful and there was hardly a whisper of breeze – but just enough to make the tall grasses dance very gently like stately ladies singing in a choir.

At the end of the garden there was an old bench where she seated herself and quite suddenly there was nothing in her

68

mind; it had decided to rest and focus on the grasses in their hypnotic dance – so very relaxing. When the cup slipped out of her hands and onto the ground below she realised she had been asleep.

When she got back to their room, Isaac was well away, so very quietly she slipped out of her "day" clothes and slid gently in beside him; he didn't move – and she was soon joining him in the deepest slumber. That night she had the strangest dream.

They had arrived in London and for some reason were in Trafalgar Square; a crowd was gathering for the subsequent arrival of a speaker; Ann, in her dream enquired who it was, and was informed that it was Humpty Dumpty who was going to prove that it was possible to sit on a wall without falling off.

When he began to speak from the platform, Isaac suddenly for no reason at all, jumped up from his sickbed and began to harangue the speaker in very ripe terms. All the while, in her dream, she was trying to get Isaac to desist; but he was well into his exhibition and along with the profanities he used, danced with great agility.

What did it all mean – or did it all mean nothing at all? Probably the latter she had thought.

When they had arrived at Great Yarmouth it was looking very much like rain, so it was decided to make straight for their lodgings; they would see the monument on the next day and which would precede their travels to Woodbridge.

Isaac was looking towards to this particular stop-over with mixed feelings; yes it would be good to see his youngest brother Joseph again and his nephew Alfred – but he wasn't sure that he wanted to see them in the position he was in.

Ann was looking forward to seeing them again because it was largely through their family in Woodbridge that Isaac and she had met at Kelvedon's Quaker Friends Meeting House; when they were both quite young. It was when Isaac was serving part of his apprenticeship with his uncle Isaac in Woodbridge. They had occasion to go to London and by the greatest good fortune, the main road from Woodbridge to London went right past Ann's mother's house in Kelvedon; the Friends Meeting House being on the other side of the road further along; many Quaker travellers along the road to and from London would stop off at The Kelvedon Quaker Meeting House; Isaac his uncle and brother Joseph being two of them.

After Isaac had made a few visits to their meeting house, the elders felt that Ann and he would make a good match and encouraged a courtship; it was all very proper and according to Quaker custom.

Eventually, when the elders of their families and the Quaker elders had assented their approval, in the Spring of 1818 they were married at The Quaker Meeting House in Kelvedon.

Was she glad she married him? Yes of course she was – but as he would remind her many a time, her sisters had all married much better prospects that him; and he was right – at the time they were married her sister's husbands were all members of established successful families; and indeed Isaac's own family was well established in Wainfleet but Isaac was not following the family business; he and elder brother Thomas had begun the milling venture in Boston.

When they had been conducting their courtship, Isaac had

kept her informed of the progress in the building of the mill; he saw it as a great venture which would secure all of their futures – and even though things had been hard – he still nursed the fond hope that a corner could be turned and the future bright and she was with him one hundred percent.

Looking back – Ann could see that spirited, determined and committed young woman of thirty-three; was she still that same woman at sixty-five?

Yes – she believed she was; only now – she was a widow woman and she must now learn to live accordingly. Though she was engaged in exercise of reflection – looking back over her life, it was the present and the future that she must give her physical and intellectual energies to. It seemed a very long way from then to now; seated as she was on a bench overlooking the Mediterranean; financially secure – she knew she would always be that – her sons would see to it. A prosperous business with new products being added almost each year but it all started off with starch; oh how we British love our starch and the stiffer the better; blouses, shirts, dresses and petticoats, sheets and pillow cases, table cloths, handkerchiefs – in fact anything in the linen line would have to be starched.

Sitting there as she was, her mind drifting along all manner of avenues, she hadn't seen James and the Chapman's walking up to her.

"Hello mother – writing your memoirs again?"
With a start, Ann turned to see them, "Oh James – I didn't see you coming; you don't seem to have been gone for long."

"Gone for long mother! Only two hours."

"Two hours! I wonder if I've been asleep."

"I shouldn't think so mother – I imagine that you have been so locked into your memories, you haven't noticed the time passing by."

"Did you enjoy the fort?"

Miss Chapman took the response, "Oh it was wonderful; James climbed to the very top of the look-out tower; wasn't he brave."

"You didn't go that far then?" asked Ann.

"No – mother and I were quite happy to enjoy the view from the lower."

"Very sensible of you; I'm sure I wouldn't have climbed the tower."

"Are you ready for a spot of lunch?"

"Yes – I'm feeling quite peckish after all the travelling I've been doing."

Miss Stafford had also recommended a place for them to eat; one which would cater for British tastes as well as providing the local cuisine. It was near to the Princess Palace where their landau was going to collect them later. Both she and James were quite happy to try new tastes but she got the impression that Mrs. Chapman was happier with English style food. Her daughter was quite happy with the French style of food; the place Miss Stafford had recommended would serve them all well.

As they made their way to the venue, Ann walked along chatting with Mrs. Chapman while James led the way with Miss Chapman, who was a ready audience for his enthusiastic chit-chat; it was mainly about the company and it's future involvement in The International Exhibition in London.

"Just listen to my darling boy; you wouldn't have thought it was the same boy who arrived three months ago. It really is a most agreeable place; the very air being the medicine; and wonder if any of the locals get ill."

"I'm sure they do Mrs. Reckitt but not the same illnesses that we encounter; I imagine that Cirrhosis of the liver would not be uncommon, judging by the amount of wine they drink."

"Ah – you're agin drinking then?"

"Oh Mrs. Reckitt – are not you – being of the Quaker faith as you are?"

"Quakers are not agin alcohol Mrs. Cooper – in fact there are a number of very well known, and successful brewers who are Quakers."

"Well – you do surprise me."

"What we are agin are over-indulgences; the total domination of people's lives through drink. Why – did not our saviour turn water into wine; which is, incidentally, what vintners do – adding grapes for the process."

"Yes I expect you're right – I never thought of it that way."

They both laughed companionably; Ann found she quite liked Mrs. Cooper. It was decided that they would have their lunch outside the café at one of the tables there; James went for the menu and they made their choices. A huge jug of fruit juice was brought to the table; it was very refreshing.

"So James – what have you been telling Miss Cooper?"

"Oh this and that mother."

"I bet it included The International Exhibition."

"Well – I did sort of mention that."

Ann thought that Miss Cooper was looking quite bright eyed.

"Oh – yes – it sounds marvellous. Mama – we really must get to see it; James' company is going to be showing off the things they make at their factory in Hull; he's told me all about it. And do you know what mama – we use some of the products they make."

"Do we?"

"Well the servants do – they make the washing starches we use – and metal polishes and the blue stuff they put into the tub to make the linens brighter; and James says his brothers are really clever and when he's better he's going to join them and they are going to make lots of other things."

"It seems that your son has made quite an impression on my little Susanna."

Ann laughed - "James is not short on enthusiasm for the firm."

"And why not mother – father put a lot of work into getting the company going."

Ann smiled to herself; yes – Isaac had put a lot of work into their ventures but it was his sons who had made the company what it was today. She remembered when they first came to Hull with very little in the way of money; they had gone into lodgings at 21 Bourne Street. Three failed business enterprises behind him but the little starch works they rented and then bought was a very good move; prior to that Isaac had several attempts at being a corn merchant and three goes at the milling business; manufacturing was a new turn – and it proved to be the makings of him – especially with four sons – old enough then to help him.

When the food arrived, conversation ceased for a while as they addressed themselves to the meal and there was plenty of it; four clean plates were soon displayed, each of them remarking how enjoyable it all was. Once the plates were removed an enormous bowl of fruit was put on the table and a cheese board, loaded with enough cheese to feed an army.

A nice snooze would have been very welcome at that moment; a practice popular with the French; they called it la sieste. Everything seems to stop for la sieste – though the restaurants keep open, almost all the shops and businesses close for a couple of hours, some even for three hours but they tended to stay open later in the afternoon and early evening. It was accepted as quite normal; Anne wondered what the people of Hull would have made of the shops and businesses closing at midday for such a long period; they would have a riot on their hands.

"Has everyone had enough to eat?"

"Well I certainly have James. What about you ladies?"
Mrs and Miss Cooper both gave signals to the effect that they had also.

"Will we all take coffee?"

The three ladies assented and James ordered it.

"So mother did the time pass agreeably for you as you waited for us to return from our great climb."

"Yes – it did James; I was recalling the time when we lived in Boston. Before you were born of course."

"Oh – you lived in Boston. How interesting. America is such a captivating place."

"If you will forgive me Mrs. Cooper but the Boston where we

75

lived was the original Boston in Lincolnshire."

"Mama – fancy you not knowing about Boston in Lincolnshire."

"Well I did know – I expect"

Slightly abashed and not terribly pleased with her daughter's admonishment, Mrs Cooper ventured, "Did you live there long?"

"A little over twelve years."

"It's quite famous for it's church – isn't it Mrs. Reckitt?"

"Well – certainly – it is quite an impressive building for such a small town."

"I read that it was the tallest parish church in England."

"It would have been taller if the builders had had their way; there was meant to be a steeple added to top the tower but the idea was put aside; people roundabout call the tower Boston Stump – but the church is St. Botolph's; the house where we lived was in the church yard."

"Tell them what you did that time when father was very sick; how you took him on a horse and cart to get him cured at Bath in Somerset."

Ann blushed slightly; James could be quite impetuous at times. "James – really; these two ladies don't want to hear about all that."

"I'm, sure they do mother; it's a wonderful story."

"Oh do please tell us about it!" pleaded Susanna.

Mrs. Cooper came to her aid, "Really Susanna – under the circumstances of Mrs. Reckitt's recent loss, perhaps it is a little perplexing for her." Anne thought that this was said for the benefit of James as much as for Mrs. Cooper's daughter.

"No – it isn't perplexing, I assure you and over the last couple of days, my thoughts have been much about that time of our lives. Even when I look back, some of it I find quite unbelievable but that is often the case when we reflect on the things we did in the past."

So in that café in Monaco, she told her tale.

It was odd in a way, that what she had considered her duty, borne out of love and loyalty to Isaac, was seen by others as akin to heroism and on reflection she could see why.

The Coopers were quite enthralled by the story; but she wondered would the same impression be formed had the roles been reversed, with Ann being the sick one and Isaac driving the cart; was it the fact that she was a woman which made for the incredulity expressed.

"But weren't you frightened at all?" questioned Miss Cooper.

"OH – there were moments when I wondered if I would be able to properly negotiate some of the bad roads and the ford river crossings; I think those especially, because if the cart had toppled over, my husband might have been tipped out into the water or the mud banks."

"But what about bands of robbers - did you not fear the possibility of being set upon."

"Well – yes and no Miss Cooper; you see, we didn't carry a lot of any great value – or over much cash and what we did have was well concealed within the mattress that Isaac was lying upon. This coupled with the fact that we avoided the hours of darkness to be on the road; and it's often in the dark hours that travellers and their belongings were parted from them. Or perhaps they saw us and decided that we looked too poor to be of any value to them. I would imagine that the rich looking stagecoaches were more in their line."

Laughter followed this last remark.

"Well I think that you were very brave Mrs. Reckitt."

Ann gave a sheepish grin, "There were those around us who would have used the word foolhardy to describe what I did; and what's more, I could see their points of view. But the old saying holds good - 'Desperate situations call for desperate measures'."

And in saying that, she wondered if anyone really appreciated just how desperate the situation was. Certainly, those around them could see that Isaac was in a bad way; they could guess for themselves just how much pain he was in but she doubted very much whether anyone apart from her really understood the full measure of his despair.

It could all so easily have been avoided – if he would have accepted the offers of financial help forthcoming from her brothers-in-law; her mother too had offered to send money; and certainly he did accept offers of financial help with regard to the business but only when he could see his way clear to the possibility of giving them a return on their investments, as Isaac saw it.

They chatted on for another half hour or so – Ann steering the conversation towards more general topics. At the agreed time and place their landau arrived to take them home; and were they all glad when it did; the heat of the day, the sumptuous lunch and the rhythm of the horse trotting soon sent each of them to the land of slumber.

It wasn't a long drive from Monaco to Menton – a little

the hour at a trot but at a slow trot more like one hour forty. Plenty enough time to have a dream; Ann had several and all involving her driving a horse and cart; once being in some kind of race – with James and Miss. Cooper in a competing cart and Isaac accompanied by Mrs. Cooper in a third. The location in the dream was the sea-shore at Bridlington, where hundreds of people were sitting around in deck chairs cheering them on. With much vigorous action on her part in the driver capacity, her cart rolled over the finishing line to great cheers from grown-ups and children on the beach but when she turned round to see how far away the others were, there was no-one to be seen; at that point she woke up to find the others all chuckling at her.

"Was I talking in my sleep?"

"Oh yes mother - you were talking alright and by the way you were waving your arms about you seemed to be engaged in some kind of battle royal."

"James – you should have wakened me!"

"Oh – but mother – you were presenting us with some quite absorbing entertainment; we thought at one time you would topple the coach!"

"Oh – Mr. Reckitt" admonished Miss Cooper, " - you go too far; it was nothing of the kind Mrs. Reckitt – though you did appear to shouting Gee-Up quite a lot!"

They were still laughing as they got down from their coach, each going to their separate rooms saying they would meet at dinner.

Ann was glad to get to her room, for despite the laughing and the great good fun they'd all enjoyed on their excursion, she knew that tears were not far away. As she closed the door behind her they weren't long in coming.

OH Isaac – why could you not now be there with me; why didn't you have the sense to realise that going back to cold damp Hull was not a good idea after being in Menton and the sun.

Why Isaac – why?

And the tears flowed.

Chapter nine

It was not as early that Ann awoke next day; but despite this fact, what sleep she had had didn't seem to have done her any good. Her mind this morning was very far from clear; though she was happy to be taking the journey through her memories; some quite painful – she was also feeling that it was time to move on; there was too much of Isaac here – not that she resented that but almost everything in the room reminded her of his recent presence.

That's maybe how it was with grief; coming to terms with the future must inevitably involve sorting out the past. Would she have changed anything? Would she have done anything differently? Both answers to these questions were the same; probably not! Isaac was a good husband and father; yes he could be immoderate in debate and headstrong in his opinions but his heart was open and huge; he had time for everyone – he cared about all his workers and knew them all by name – and their wives and children as well; James was going to be the model of his father – though his thinking head would be more orderly; Isaac had been a bit of a dreamer – for the best possible reasons of course; James was going to be a dreamer as well – but his dreams were going to have a more well thought out edge to them; and he knew full well that she would support him and be there to guide him when he required guidance.

Some day, in the not too distant future, James would marry and she would be very happy to see that happen; not that she wanted to be free of him, for she would always be his mother no matter what; she would always have his interests at heart – as she would of all her son's and daughter of course; dearest Bessie – who would take her father's death the hardest of all her little brood.

What had she herself felt when her own father had died? She was just six years of age – and though she was sad – there had not been the years of life with her father that Elizabeth had with Isaac.

Two years after his death, her mother had remarried; but there was not the faintest chance that Ann would marry again. She had no need for the financial support of a husband – and she certainly would not be considering having more children; that is if it was physically possible. There would be plenty to occupy her time; her interest in the business, not on the manufacturing side of course – but in the welfare aspects of it; the workers and their needs had been, in the past and would be in the future, something in which she would continue to be involved; that their workers should have the benefit of an education – albeit a rudimentary education, was in Ann's opinion, essential; a view not shared with everyone in her wide circle of friends and acquaintances – many of whom were still of the opinion that being able to read and write was of little use to the working classes; and what was more, so they said, it gave them ideas above their station and engendered resentment and discontent.

Not the case, of course, if anything quite the opposite; the feeling of self worth could only be beneficial to the business as it was to themselves and their families; and so she would continue with her work with the employees and their families; it would be what Isaac would have wanted and her son's approved of it and knew the value of her efforts as well as anyone.

It would be very tempting to cut short their stay and hurry back to Hull, where she could immerse herself into the everyday necessities of life; she would be kept busy; of that fact she was quite sure – part of her welcomed that idea.

However, there were other considerations, not the least of which being, James' health improvement, which was going quite well and should be allowed to take its full course.

But at breakfast, she would tell him of her thinking; that they might move on to another part of the Riviera – for indeed, as Dr. Bennett pointed out in his book, the health benefits were felt throughout this region – they could move on to other places; and be driven there – not like her journey with the sick and paralysed Isaac, where she'd had to do the driving, as well as everything else.

After breakfast they informed Miss Stamford that they would be moving on to see other parts of the Riviera; she said she could be sorry to see them go but quite understood their reasoning. There would be no problem in filling their space – in fact – she had quite a little list of visitors would be delighted to occupy the rooms that they would vacate.

Mrs. Cooper and he expressed themselves as being a little dismayed that James and she would be moving on and for a moment Ann got the very distinct feeling that the Coopers would like to be moving on with themselves; with that there would be the inevitability of Miss. Cooper becoming even more smitten with James, of which she was fairly certain, there could be no future – they not being of the Quaker belief.

For the week that followed the giving of their notice – Ann gave as much time as she could, to her thoughts and reminiscences; there was part of her that felt this was by far the wisest and healthiest thing to do. Not that the process would not continue when they returned to Hull but this seemed the right course to follow at the present time.

Her daily walks around the beautiful avenues and lanes of Menton, which would have been taken with Isaac, she now resumed – sometimes with James by her side, sometimes alone. It seemed that at each spot where she and Isaac had sat and rested for a while, there was a special memory to be experienced.

Sitting watching the boats in the harbour reminded her very much of Woodbridge; boats of all shapes and sizes bobbing in and out. Woodbridge was the next stop on their journey to Bath but they almost didn't make it.

Some of the roads in that part of Suffolk were in a bad state of repair and much rutted; attempts were made by the local road-men to keep them passable but in the main that was for much bigger carts than theirs; and ones which could accommodate the ruts and pot-holes more readily.

Dobbin did his best and at times Ann got off the cart to walk alongside him to relieve him of some of the weight; it was whilst she was doing this on a particularly deserted stretch of road that, distracted by two squabbling blackbirds in the nearby hedgerow, she hadn't noticed a deep rut was upon them; they were on it before she had time to steer Dobbin clear of the hazard and over they went – Dobbin and all. Poor Isaac was tossed into the hedgerow ditch and the mattress ended up on top of him; Dobbin lying on his side was kicking and making a pitiful racket at the same time as trying to free himself from the shafts. Quickly she made sure that Isaac was alright; well – as alright as he could be having being tossed so violently off the cart. He had told he she must see to Dobbin first, which she did as best she could; it was quite frightening for her because, even though he was no young beast, one kick from his powerful legs could render her unconscious. Dobbin's frantic attempts to break free of his bindings only succeeded in making the straps tighter; she would have to calm him down before she could do anything in any practical way to free him. Poor Dobbin – she felt like crying herself but she knew that wasn't going to do any good so she just talked to him and occasionally tried stroking him until he calmed down. For all she knew he could have sustained broken bones; as indeed Isaac might have – though she felt not. It seemed like hours before the distressed horse was calm enough to allow her to unloose the straps. Once free his first instinct was to run away and despite her frantic calls to him to come back – he made headlong for the road ahead and soon disappeared out of sight around a bend.

"Dobbin – come back – Dobbin – come back – we need you – DOBBIN!

Isaac was only able to see a little of what was happening but he made a fairly accurate assessment of the situation. Ann came over the where he was lying and climbed down into the ditch which, as chance would have it, was dry.

"Are you hurt Isaac?"

"I'm not sure Ann – when a body is in pain most of the time it's difficult to know if anything additional has been added."

"Oh Isaac – I was so stupid – I should have looked where we were going."

"It's not your fault Ann – the roads are so bad in places and you weren't to know we were going to topple over."

"If I hadn't let myself be distracted by those squabbling blackbirds I would have seen the rut."

"The road is practically made of ruts - it would have been bound to happen sooner or later."

"Are you quite sure that you're alright Isaac?"

"Yes – I'm as sure as I can be; but I rather think that I'd prefer not to spend the night in this ditch – even with the benefit of the mattress."

"OH – Isaac – how can you joke at a time like this?"

"Why not? It could be worse – Dobbin could have fallen on top of me." What, with the shock and the fear, Ann suddenly broke out laughing, she knew it was silly to be laughing but she just couldn't stop – Isaac joined in and soon the pair of them were helpless with hysterics; Anne was laughing so wildly that she found herself dropping to her knees and eventually toppling deeper into the ditch with Isaac - which only succeeded in making them both laugh even louder.

Isaac clapped his arms round her and pulled her to him and then the laughter turned to tears, which were bound to come.

"Come Ann – you were laughing but a minute ago – why the tears?"

And through her sobbing, he could just about detect the words she was saying.

"OH – Isaac – I could have lost you."

He stroked her hair and drew her closer to him.

"Yes – well – it could have been a lot worse; but I'm alright – a few bruises no doubt – but nothing life threatening; and judging by the way Dobbin has bolted off down the road – there can't be much injury to him either."

Her sobbing subsided.

"But how are we going to get him back?"

"Well – there's some rope in the back of the cart – you could do like the horse breakers do and see if you can lasso him."

The incongruity of this set them both laughing again and Ann fell against him. In their 'jollifications' they hadn't noticed a figure standing up above the ditch and looking down at them.

He was a rather rotund gentleman dressed in a brown smock and wearing leggings tied up at the knees; he had a mass of wild looking hair upon which a cap, much too small for him was perched.

"Excuse me – have you lost a horse?"

Startled, they both looked up at the vision above them.

Once again he addressed them - "Well – have you?" They looked at each other as if to say -

"Well – I suppose we have?" - and that set them both off laughing again.

This seemed to cause the visitor a certain amount of indignation and the broad whiskers which seem to go out from beneath his nose and reach almost to his shoulders, seemed to reflect his mood.

"Well – if all you want to do is lay about laughing – I'll be on my way then!"

At that – Ann jumped up to her feet and scrambled up the ditch, straightening herself and freeing herself from the leaves and grass clinging to her skirts, apologising as she did so.

She then noticed that the gentleman with the enormous whiskers was not alone; another – similarly attired but with not such a grand hirsute, was at the other side of the road holding onto Dobbin.

"Dobbin – you've come back – OH Dobbin – I'm so sorry for not looking where we were going."

She then realised that both these men, who could very well have been brothers, were looking at her.

"OH – I'm sorry – I should have thanked you for bringing Dobbin back; I don't know how I would have managed it."

"What be the matter with your man?"

Ann looked down at Isaac still lying there.

"I'm afraid my 'man' is in a poor state of physical health."

At that Isaac began to attempt an exit from the ditch; trying to drag himself up with his arms.

"Isaac – stay there I'll come down."

"Stay where you are missus - me and Albert'll there'll get him out; come on Albert; missus – you take the horse." Ann did as she was bidden and the two gentlemen began the task of getting Isaac out.

It was a bit of a struggle for them due to Isaac not being able to do a great deal for himself but eventually they got him up to the road level.

"We'll need to lay him down on the mattress, if you will help please – he's suffering from paralysis in his legs."

"If you could just get me onto the mattress – I'll be alright for a while." Isaac said.

"Right then – Albert – you grab the mattress and I'll be a keepin' 'old of him meanwhile."

Albert performed the task as bidden and Isaac was laid down with the pillows, which had also been tossed out of the cart, under his head.

"You alright now mister?"

"Yes – thank you; we're very fortunate you happened by."

"Nothin' fortunate about it – they horse led us back to you." Ann gave Dobbin a hug.

"Where you be biding for then?" asked long whiskers. Ann came in -

"Well – we're hoping to eventually get to Bath."

"Well – if you be wanting a bath we can sort you out with that down at the farm house; though we don't use it more'n once a month. It ain't healthy."

Their rescuer was so droll and yet so very kind that Ann didn't really want to make him feel foolish; well – not everyone knew about Bath the place; she decided, after some thought, on claiming that she hadn't known there was a place called Bath till someone told her – which was in a way partly true.

He looked at her enquiringly and said "Eh!" Ann realised that she was going to have to relate the whole story to him and this she did, to which he replied.

"Well – I'm blowed! What do you say Albert?"

"Never not heard nothing like it in my life afore!"

"Well." declared long whiskers, "I reckon that you is one very spunky lady; ain't that so Albert?"

"Tis an' all Billy; never heard the like afore."

Isaac hearing his wife's praises sung out, felt it was incumbent upon him to add his own thoughts.

"Ann is a wife in a thousand."

In one way, Ann was secretly pleased to hear her praises sung, but in another way she felt a sense of abashment at hearing the words declared so boldly.

"I'm just a woman like any other woman and I do what I have to do – as I see it." And she changed the subject to the state of the cart.

"I wonder how we can get this fixed," she declared to nobody in particular.

"You don't worry your head about that missus – first thing we must do is get you some place to rest a while."

"But we were on our way to Woodbridge."

"Well – you won't be getting to Woodbridge tonight; indeed you won't – not driving your cart like the way what it is; Albert's brother is a joiner and wheelwright – we'll get him to have a look at it for you."

Ann was somewhat taken aback at the way Billy had appeared to take control of the situation; she looked to Isaac for some sort of input but he just shrugged his shoulders.

Eventually words came, "I don't know what to say; you seem to be very much in charge of the situation – and naturally Isaac and myself are very grateful for any help you can give us but we are expected at our cousin's house in Woodbridge later today."

"Well – you just give us the address and Albert'll ride out and let 'em know what's what."

"You are most kind."

"Tis nothing missus – only too glad to help. Right then – first things first – let's get you and your man to the cottage – it's just round the bend in the road – me and Albert can carry him – if you can bring along anything you need for the night; then we'll come back with Albert's brother to recover the cart and your horse; we'll just tie him up to the gate there; he'll come to no harm and there's plenty of grass he can chew on.

So that was that thought Ann – everything seemed to be now in the hands of their new friend Billy; she wondered at the time if he was one of the Quaker faith and as it turned out he was – as was all his family.

They were given a very comfortable room in the cottage – which was (a) very big for a cottage; with so many additions to it – it seemed like it would become a mansion house very soon.

William and his wife Joanna had seven children – the eldest being fourteen and the youngest just six months old.
She enjoyed a good meal with the family before it was time for bed; Isaac had his meal on a tray, which she took to him; he'd gone very quiet; he was a man in deep thought.

Ann knew that when they were both settling down for the night there would be words from Isaac; she could tell from the way he looked at her and if looks could say words, Isaac certainly had a lot to say; she was not wrong in her guesses. As she climbed into bed alongside him she ventured, "How are you feeling now Isaac – has some of the pain eased off."

"My bodily pain has eased considerably thanks to the warm bath and your massage but the pain that is within has increased a hundredfold; Ann – we must turn back. I can't put you through this on the slender hope that treatment at Bath will cure me. You know I've never fully been in favour of this from the word go; ever since you came back from the market that day after gossiping to Abigail."

Oh dear – there were so many things she wanted to tell him – so many things she wanted to say – which she knew would be true but would have little or no effect upon him; on the contrary the things she wanted to say could well have an adverse effect. Isaac was a good man and a considerate husband but she felt she wanted to say to him that it was not just for her he wanted them to turn back but for his own pride; his own discomfiture at having to have everything done for him. But if only he would realise, that would be the way things would have to be if they went back to Boston. One thing was for certain – he could not work alongside his brother at the mill, so an extra wage would have to be found; what's more – someone to fill Isaac's shoes wouldn't come cheap. Well she must say something but she must tread very carefully if she was not to incur his wrath.

"Am I not your wife Isaac?"

"Yes – you are my wife."

"And when we got married – did you say that life would be a bed of roses for me?"

"No Ann – I didn't promise that – but I did promise to love, honour and cherish you."

"And so you have Isaac – so you have; this thing that has taken your body so badly – is not of your making; you did not bring it upon yourself – and you do love, honour and cherish me as I do you."

"You don't deserve it Ann – you should have had an easier life – like your sisters; they have married well." She felt she was going to lose her temper but she must stay calm; but this old chestnut came up again and again – yes her sisters had married well – and certainly their lives were a lot less stressful than her own but why could he not see that was not a life she craved; yes – she would have been delighted if Isaac had maintained good health and not sustained the crippling condition which had come upon him; yes – she would have been glad to see him free of the financial worries he bore with regard to the mill. But Isaac and his brother were not alone in their plight – many many millers throughout the county were experiencing the same thing; the infuriating Corn Laws – set up for the benefit of the farmers and the people, had achieved the opposite effect. She wanted to say all of this to him but instead opted for; "Isaac – I also promised to love and cherish you – and further more I made the promise to do so in sickness and in health as long as we both shall live."

"Then if I was to die – you would have no worries."

At this point she really wanted to hit him; he could be so infuriating at times. Instead she drew him closer to her laying his head upon her breast.

"Isaac – you must never say anything like that to me again."

"I'm sorry Ann – I'm such a fool and I know I let my tongue run away with me at times – but if only you knew how it pains my heart to see you having to put up with this useless husband you have acquired."

OH dear – he really was feeling low but how could she bring him out of his despair; how could she change the course of his thinking – how could she restore his confidence and at the same time restore some of her own – which, at that moment, was at a low ebb as well. Nothing would have been simpler than for her to say - "Yes – you're right Isaac – it's all too much for me – I don't deserve all this aggravation and discomfort; yes – let's go back to Boston and watch you getting worse and worse; till the disease spreads to your arms and then your hands and fingers – til you won't be able to do anything at all for yourself.

She stroked his cheek and pushed his hair back out of his eyes. OH how very much she loved this infuriating man.

"Isaac – my own dear husband – tomorrow is another day; and tomorrow we will do great things and the day after that and the day after that; but some days won't be so great at all – some days we will feel that it's all too much. But we have God on our side – we have a family who love us; we want the best for them and we will give it to them."

She turned his head towards her and she looked him full in the eyes.

"If it's alright with you Isaac – I want to believe in you; you have imaginative ideas and you have amazing ambition – both of which will come together at some time in the not too distant future and we will never look back."

"Ann you really arn't a wife in a thousand – you're a wife in ten thousand."

Chapter ten

Woodbridge seemed to be a much bigger place than Ann had remembered it and at first she was confused as to which road led to Isaac's cousin's house. It had been twelve years since they had visited Woodbridge. Isaac didn't seem to remember the place too well either. He seemed to think that their house was somewhere near the old tide mill; and certainly it was still there and in good working order. Folk in Woodbridge are very proud of their tidal mill which makes very good use of the natural tide rise and fall; her father had talked a lot about this inventive structure and how it operated without wind which gave a better guarantee of work; quite a rarity around those parts.

After wandering around the town and asking people directions they arrived at the Friends Meeting House in Turn Lane; there they were able to get directions to the home of Isaac's relatives – who were expecting them – though not down to any specific day or time. They made Isaac and Ann very welcome and though they were only family by marriage they treated Ann as if she was one of their own and marvelled at her strength of purpose in the task she had set herself to.

It was good to see them again yet, though they tried to disguise it, when they saw Isaac's condition, she could detect the great concern they were not able to hide.

They were pressed upon to stay longer - and as Ann recalled, it was very tempting to accept their offer, yet she knew they must move on – ever nearer to the place where Ann felt in her inner-most being, would be the turning point of their lives.

From Woodbridge to Kelvedon was a good twelve hours drive but the roads were much better, being the main route to London from that part of the country and it was almost a straight run to "The Lawns" - the name given to the house that was Ann's former home in Kelvedon. Her mother had a great affection for Isaac and she knew that there would be a truly warm welcome awaiting them when they arrived; no doubt her sisters would visit along with their husbands and though she would be delighted to see them all again, she knew that it would not be easy for Isaac to be seen in his present condition. As they made their way along the London Road, Ann could not but recall how Isaac had said to her that her sisters had made better marriages than she had.

She could not deny that Edward Gripper, Robert Ransome, and John Morland, her sisters' husbands, had been successful in their dealings but Isaac's time would come – she'd told him that over and over again; but his illness had brought him very low in his spirit and she earnestly prayed that the meeting with his brothers in law would not bring him any more distress. Ann also knew that at a word any one of them would give him any financial help he needed; indeed her own mother had always expressed herself that she was more than happy to advance him funds at any time. But Isaac was a very independent man and he had his pride, which she knew he would deny strongly, considering pride to be a sin; Isaac would describe what he felt as self-respect. But he did always say that when the time was right he would be more than happy to accept financial investment in his business but only on the condition that it was to be regarded as an investment and not a charitable gift.

That was Isaac – her beloved Isaac and would she have him any other way? No – that was the Isaac she loved and cared for; the man she married in Kelvedon twelve years ago. If only, if only he could get better, there was nothing that Isaac could not achieve for he had a heart for making a good future for his family and helping others along the way.

As the cart trundled along the road – Dobbin faithfully pulling them ever onward, she knew that marrying Isaac had been the right decision; she just knew that the future held something great and good for all of them. But as Isaac would say, "The really great things in life are never easily gained but the will to succeed and a firm purpose were vital."

They were now on The London Road – the road Isaac, his cousin and his uncle had driven along to visit with them and the Friends Meeting House; the same road Isaac and his family had travelled along to Kelvedon and their wedding; the road Isaac had driven them both along back to Boston and their lives together.

Bringing herself back to the present, Ann was suddenly filled with acute sadness at the thought that she and Isaac would never travel along that road again. She may yet visit Kelvedon many times but never again with Isaac.

Though the day was bright - there was a breeze blowing

across the harbour at Menton and it brought with it a slight chill; this along with the emotional chill she felt at that moment and not having brought with her a shawl, she decided to make her way back to the pension. Her fob watch told her that it was getting towards lunchtime anyway so she would just have time to wash her hands and face before making for the dining room.

It hadn't occurred to her what James had been up to whilst she had been whiling away the time down at the harbour. As she was nearing the house she realised that James was walking down the hill towards her; he looked quite concerned.

"Mother – we have all been looking for you."

"Looking for me James – whatever for – has there been some sort of catastrophe?"

"No but you had been gone so long and someone said they had seen you by the harbour."

"Yes James – that's where I have been; for rather longer than I intended it's true but there didn't seem to be any pressing urgency to get back; we had no arrangement for doing anything in particular this morning."

"But I worry about you mother."

"Well you have no need to."

"Yes – but ....."

"But nothing James. I am here – alive and well; I have not been captured by pirates and whisked off to be the slave bride of some middle eastern despot."

At this James could not help but burst out laughing – as much from relief as from his mother's jesting.

"The question is - who would be slave to whom? I can't see

you being anybody's slave mother."

"Not even yours?"

His face dropped.

"I'm teasing James – just teasing."

Teasing she may have been but she knew deep within her that in a way, she would be his slave – that was until the day he married; and after that she wondered if ever she could cease being so. Though it was a self- imposed devotion and not really slavery she knew that her life from now on would be lived, to a very large extent, for James. Oh – she loved and was devoted to the others in her flock, but she knew that James, her youngest, would have claim to a very major chunk of her heart. But God willing, he would marry and then – yes what then? But first she must get him well – as she had done for his father.

That day the luncheon was excellent for a change and plenty of it; in fact they were both so full she and James decided that a snooze was in order. An after lunch siesta being much loved by the French; it was not unusual to see bodies in various positions of somnolence, all over the place. Ann was quite shocked at first to find the locals just curled up under a tree and fell fast asleep; most didn't even have a cover over them – they just took their slumber where they may. Most families, however would have day beds, which for the remainder of the day passed as chaise longues. Their bedrooms at the pension each had a chaise longue for the facility of taking an afternoon nap and after their substantial lunch Ann and her son retired to their respective bedrooms to take advantage of that provision.

Ann may have felt quite sleepy – but her mind was too active to allow for actual deep sleep and she dozed fitfully having short and disturbing dreams, most of them centring on her childhood and in particular the time surrounding her father's death.

How incredibly strong her mother had been; they had their proper period of mourning and as a family expressed their sorrows but the future had to be addressed – as indeed her own future now would need to be addressed. There was much to do – not quite as much as her mother had to face; to lose a husband at such a young age and with a family to support was a considerable challenge for any woman and to leave the comparative security of familiar surroundings with the presence of family nearby was something which must have taken a great deal of courage. From Cley to Kelvedon was no mean distance – some hundred miles or more. But she did it – with her little flock and set herself to teaching Quaker girls in the area; fortunately the house they acquired, with financial help from friends, was sufficient enough to accommodate them all and the Friends Meeting House was nearby if she needed extra space.

And there at Lawn House, she had remained until her marriage to Isaac and their first home in Boston. That day she had driven them from Woodbridge to Kelvedon had been a very long day – a long and tiring day; true the road was straight enough but due to the very dry weather, was exceedingly dusty. They were regularly overtaken by carts and traps being driven at a much faster pace than they were travelling at, throwing up the inevitable dust off the road as they went by. But at least she had the security of knowing that at the end of this stretch of their journey there would be the promise of a hot bath.

They passed through one of her favourites cities – Colchester but apart from a brief stop to eat the food they had been provided with by Isaac's cousins, there was no time to do any sightseeing. They must get to Kelvedon before dark – and then they would take a couple of days as a breather and Dobbin could have a good rest. They would be more than half way to Bath when they reached Kelvedon.

Two days stopover was all she had allowed but she didn't doubt for one minute that her mother would try to persuade them to stay a little longer; and as she drove through Colchester, admiring the great architectural variety, and splendour of the city, she knew she would more than likely give in to her mother's wishes.

They would have a great deal to talk about and no doubt a family gathering would bring news of things that didn't always get included in letters. Her main concern was, as she had expressed to herself previously, that Isaac would be able to handle all the attention they would get. Such being out of love and concern for them was never in doubt but it might just be that some of it could be seen by Isaac as intrusive.

But her family was her family – and very precious to her; she recognised that each one had an individual personality as she had herself. Each was a good person, within their own sphere of goodness and each of them knew they would do anything for each other. But she had to just take things as they came; maybe her concerns would be unfounded – maybe Isaac would take everything in his stride and see everything in a generous light.

Kelvedon four miles read the milestone at the side of the road; another hour or thereabouts, would bring them to their hot baths. Isaac would be bathed first and she would get him straight into bed; perhaps mother would be happy for him remain there for the night and she would be allowed to take his supper up to him. Isaac would appreciate that; tomorrow he would be able to give his fuller attention to the chatter and conversation which would ensue.

It was dusk by the time they arrived and she was very tired; a bed to fall into would have been the thing she most desired but that would have to wait until Isaac had been attended to and they had both had some food.

Apart from the general greetings and hugs, they were spared anything to report of any great length; that would be left until the next day and no one protested when, after their baths and a good supper, she and Isaac took themselves off to their bed. Though overcome by tiredness, neither of them seemed to be able to make for sleep straight away; it was the location that for both of them had triggered off memories.

"It's twelve years since we were last here – that being for our marriage; it seems such a short time but in many ways it seems a long time ago as well."

"I know Isaac – much the same thing was going through my mind. But I remember very well the first time you came to our Sunday worship; you and your cousin."

"I thought you might have been more inclined towards him than me; his family being so well thought of in Woodbridge."

"How do you know I wasn't more inclined towards him?" she chafed him playfully.

"You'd have done a lot better if you had."

"What – and never had the children you have given me?"

"I wonder how they are all faring without us."

"I should think they'll be faring very well; Bessie will see to that – they won't get away with much either; she'll keep our rascally boys in good order."

"She's your daughter Ann – you to a T!"

Ann played with those thoughts for a moment before she responded to what Isaac had said. Was Bessie so much like herself? It sometimes takes another person to see how your personality reflects in your children. But the fact was – they were in very capable hands with her eldest; she would see that they came to no harm but would be quite firm. Ann had always encouraged her children to be individuals – to express their own views but to respect other people's views as well. But she brought them up to ultimately respect the decisions of their parents as being the best for them.

Sometimes this met with a measure of opposition from the boys, who from time to time stretched her patience; not because they were particularly badly behaved – far from it but because they were so full of life and not infrequently mischievous; having an adventure they would describe their antics and she smiled as she recalled some of their adventures; adventures which at the time made her frantic with worry – their playground including The Haven the tidal river which flowed almost at the rear of their property in Boston.

"My daughter to a T – yes – I expect she is; but she also has many of your ways too Isaac."

"Yes – all her bad habits I suppose."

"Not at all."

She gave him a hug of reassurance.

"I was wondering if the boys were trying to have any of their adventures."

"You can be sure of it dearest wife but Bessie will keep them in line and you can most certainly be sure of that."

"They can be very persuasive."

"And so can Bessie when the need arises."

"She certainly can, but you know Isaac, they will try."

"They will Ann – they will; and we must try to get some sleep. Goodnight my dearest wife."

"Goodnight husband."

They gave each other a goodnight kiss and settled themselves down in the lovely soft bed. Isaac was soon snoring but Ann didn't seem to be able to catch her sleep. Her children were now presenting themselves one by one before her and she seemed to be looking at each of them in turn and wondering if she had done the right thing in leaving them. But Isaac had needed her – of that she was certain; but her children needed her as well. Had she neglected them in favour of their father. No one had out-rightly accused her of that but some comments made by her friends and family seemed to her to have been hinting at this.

Had she been reckless in her actions? Was it such a good idea to set off on this journey under the circumstances? Had she really thought the whole thing through properly?

It wasn't too late to turn back; yes she would have to admit to the doubters that they had been right; she would have to swallow her pride. And who knew – Isaac might get better once the Summer was with them. His doctor in Boston had said as much – he didn't hold a lot of confidence in the hydrotherapy treatments.

But she had argued against all of this and nailed her colours to the mast – but which flag was she flying now? Was she getting cold feet – was she ready give it all up?

Chapter eleven

Sleep would not come, not helped by Isaac's snoring, so there was nothing for it but to quietly slide out of the bed, pop her feet into her slippers and head for the kitchen to make herself a warm drink.

Her mother hadn't yet turned in and she also was in the kitchen having a night-cap.

"Couldn't sleep mother; I think maybe I'm so tired that I'm past sleep."

"It doesn't surprise me Ann – there is only just so much a body can take and you having been pushing yours to the very limits."

"You think I've been foolish – don't you?"

Her mother placed her arm around her daughter's shoulder.

"I don't think anything of the kind; I've brought you all up to be free-thinking individuals and providing you can satisfy your own convictions – then what should it matter what anyone else thinks."

"It shouldn't matter at all mother – but right at this moment my original convictions are in the balance; and I'm the one who's put them there – and no one else."

Elizabeth smiled at this very independent daughter of hers; so very much like her own self in an abundance of ways.

"OH Ann – are you absolutely sure of that?"

It was difficult for her to look into her mother's face and not feel that she was still that small girl again – albeit fiercely independent and strong willed. She went over to the larder and took out the milk jug, pouring some into a pan and putting it onto the hob; then reached up to the mantelpiece where the nutmeg was kept and grated some into the milk.

Ann remembered herself doing all these things as if it was only yesterday. She could still see her mother's face – such a lovely face graced with her usual tender smile; her hair as always tied back but with wisps of hair escaping here and there and falling around her ears and neck.

As she lay there upon the chaise longue in the bedroom of the Menton pension she felt she would like her mother to be here now. She would talk to her as one grown woman to another – yes – one widow to another; her mother had been widowed twice over. But sadly her mother had been taken to her maker for some three years now.

The words rang through her head "OH Ann – are you absolutely sure of that." Recalling that moment from the past she considered that at the time she wasn't really certain that she was absolutely sure of anything.

She had put it down to the particularly long day they had both endured; and yes – she was tired – very tired and even though they had only been on the road for not quite a week it had been a hard week; not only the tiring task of driving the cart or lifting Isaac on and off the cart; but the effort she was having to make to keep Isaac's spirits up – keep him focussed; looking back she wasn't sure at all just how focussed she was herself.

Once she'd made her hot drink she seated herself at the kitchen table; her mother, also seated at the table, had said nothing else all the while she was getting the milk and making the drink; now the both of them were facing each other.

"The honest truth is mother – that I'm not sure of anything anymore. I and I alone have set myself the task which I am undertaking and it is founded upon the love I have for Isaac and the desire to see him happy and well once more. Yes – in truth – I cannot ignore what people have said; most of it out of genuine concern and I'm sure you would agree with some of it."

"Ann – you are not a child any more and what I or anyone else thinks or doesn't think doesn't really matter, providing that you have the courage of your convictions."

"I expect that's half the trouble – one part of my head thinks one thing but the rest of my body and the other part of my brain, thinks another; it all seemed so straight forward at the first but ...."

She had been making a determined effort not to cry but it was in vain; down came the tears splashing onto the scrubbed surface of the kitchen table. There was nothing else said for a while they both continued with their drinks.

"Do you feel better for that Ann?" her mother now wiping the tears from her cheeks with a tea cloth which was lying on the table.

"Not a lot mother." She raised herself up from the kitchen chair and made to go. " I'd better go – Isaac may have wakened and wondered where I am."

Her mother came to her side and held her close; Ann's arms

immediately encircled her and she laid her head on her shoulder; there were no more tears – just the warm feeling of comfort she always experienced when she was close to her mother.

"Let's both sit down again and talk it over. Isaac will call out for you if he needs you."

Ann seated herself at the table – her mother sitting on the other side – and taking Ann's hands into her own began to speak very softly to her.

"If I'd had the chance to do anything for your father that would have kept him alive – I would have done it gladly. In a way I almost envy you for the chance you have been given to make a difference in your lives; at least you still have Isaac and I know full well how much you love him as I'm sure he does you."

Ann's eyes filled up again at her mother's wise gentle words – she squeezed her mother's hand.

"Yes – at least I have him; sick as he is – he is alive; it must have been awful for you – so young with six daughters to lose your man and then in no time at all to lose another husband. Maybe I was too young to really grasp fully what you suffered but I feel that I do now."

"So there you are then – now let's have what's really troubling you."

"I expect it's a lot to do with the fact that I feel I've pushed Isaac into this endeavour."

"Encouraged might be a better way of putting it."

"That's very generous of you mother - yes - let's say I've encouraged him with a great deal of vigour; but there's always a nagging tiny little doubt in this silly head of mine – that it will all come to nothing; that we'll get to Bath and the cure won't work – won't make a ha'porth of difference to his condition."

Elizabeth looked at her daughter quite steadily.

"Fine – so what if you do give up now – go back and tell everyone you were beaten by your misgivings; that the faith you had, failed you; because almost anything undertaken in life needs to have at least 75% faith – or a belief; a faith or a belief in a positive, successful, outcome."

"Most of the time I have that but sometimes it fails me; I'm dreading driving through London – I shall end up tipping us both in the Thames."

This brought chuckles to both of them.

"Go on with you Ann – you'll do nothing of the sort; anyway – George Milligan, who you will remember is our local haulier, is going to sit on the riding board with you and get you through the city and onto The Bath road – he'll also be giving you details of some places where you can stay over-night. He does the route quite often."

Ann's face lit up.

"OH mother – that's wonderful; how can I ever thank you enough?"

"Well for one thing – you can let me give you some money to help with any expenses."

"But mother – Isaac would never agree to that."

"Yes - I thought you might say that but does he have to know?"

"We have no secrets from each other mother."

This was a difficult one for Elizabeth – she didn't want to be seen as to be encouraging her daughter to be deceitful but on the other hand she didn't want her to be faced with a crisis either; not when a lifeline could be provided for such a contingency.

"But could you not put it to him that I'm offering to provide an emergency fund – which would be repaid when you have been to Bath – got the cure and are returning home. You can drop it off as you are passing."

"Well – putting it like that – he may agree; it certainly makes a lot of sense to me and I thank you from the bottom of my heart for your kindness."

"Let's say no more tonight – we've both finished our drinks – and you certainly need some sleep; we'll make breakfast later in the morning – I have no pupils to see tomorrow – school is closed for a couple of days."

Ann wondered how she would ever survive without her mother but eventually she knew she have to learn how to.

"Thank you again mother; but mostly for being my mother."

"For that – I need no thanks Ann – but you have all been brought up to say thank you for things given; being your mother and you being my daughter is a two way thing."

They both hugged each other and Ann made her way back to the bedroom; Elizabeth watched her go – and made a silent prayer for common sense to prevail.

Chapter twelve

Day two of the stop over at Kelvedon was almost totally taken up with visits from her sisters and their husbands. A great deal of discussion took place between Isaac and the men, whilst Anne and her sisters caught up with each other's news. There was a piece of Anne that would have liked to have been in on the debating going on in the bedroom; she did harbour a fear that it might be unhelpful to Isaac being, in the position he was; but after they had all left and Anne was able to have time on her own with Isaac, she was amazed to see how buoyant and cheerful he looked.

"I'm glad to see you looking so happy Isaac."

"Well – happy is a curious way of describing my mood Anne but I would say that since I have spoken with my brothers-in-law there is certainly a sense of peace of mind with me."

She smiled at him; it was really wonderful to, again, hear him talking this way; but she wanted to know more.

"OH – and what brought on this sense of peace of mind?"

"Just men's talk Anne – business and so on."

When he spoke like this to her she was sometimes inclined to want to box his ears.

"Just men's talk. Well – perhaps I could stick on a false beard and smoke a cigar!"

He chuckled at her and beckoned her to him.

"Come here my curious lady."

She came over to him and placed herself on the edge of the bed.

"Do you know – I can't imagine you wearing a beard and as for cigars; they are dreadful things."

She chuckled too but she was still somewhat rankled, saying nothing in reply.

"OK" he began, getting himself into a more comfortable position, "Our brothers-in-law, at our confab, think there might be a brighter prospect for us if we made a move from Boston; they think that perhaps our fortunes would be better served elsewhere; Nottingham has been suggested."

"But what about the mill?"

"Yes – well – as you know – things haven't been going too well in that direction. Some of this has been partly due to my own physical indisposition but had I been well enough – there wasn't a great deal of business for me to attend to; in short Anne – due to numerous factors – activity at the mill isn't as vigorous as it could be."

"So it's to be yet another new venture Isaac."

She was thinking back to several other of Isaac's failed endeavours.

"If you put it like that – yes – another new venture. What's more, some financial investment has been offered and I could sell my share in the mill; and Nottingham being a major town."

"I can see you're sold on the idea; naturally I will be your support in whatever you do." Despite a some misgiving she tried to be encouraging.

"Who knows, a new place, new, challenges, new prospects."

"I wonder how the children will react."

"We'll tell the boys they can join Robin Hood in Sherwood forest."

Now she did laugh and this cleared the air; she leaned over to him, propped up as he was by his pillows and gave him the very sweetest of kisses; his arms went about her and he held her close to him.

"OH Anne – you are the very best of wives."

"If you say so Isaac – if you say so." and the matter was left at that.

Next day Anne's mother was as good as her word, she had spoken to George Milligan who'd said he'd be only too happy to be of service to the young couple; and there he was – knocking on the door bright and early ready for the task in hand. In fact, George had told Elizabeth that he would be prepared to go along with them to Bath and get a lift back from there. She thanked him for this kind offer but, thinking of Anne's possible reaction, said that getting them through London would be enough.

Farewells said – hugs shared and they were soon on their way; George had offered to take the reins but Anne assured him that she would be able to manage and that giving her directions would be greatly appreciated.

As she thought back to those days she tried to recall what had made her decline the kind offer to take the reins. But try as she might she couldn't pin anything down to a specific reason; perhaps it was just the fact that she herself wanted to do this for Isaac and somehow, letting George take the reins would be in some way letting her determination down.

Her two days at Lawn House had promoted a new understanding of herself; it was often so when she had spent time with her mother, for whom she had a great deal of respect and admiration. It was almost as if some facet of her own personality was inherited from her mother and each time they met, a little more was revealed, a little more rubbed off onto her. That was not to say that she felt she would ever possess, entirely, all of her mother's qualities and strengths; she could never think of her mother in terms of weakness, for even though now a four times over mother herself, she considered it quite amazing that her own mother had dealt so well with the disproportionate measure of struggle life had brought her.

George Milligan was to journey with them as far as Hyde Park Corner which would then put them on The Bath Road; which according to George, would be plain sailing for them all the way to Bath. A list of addresses had been supplied by him which were places where some of the drivers stayed overnight; the one's that didn't sleep under their carts that is. Up to now, most of the people they had lodged with, were family friends or friends of friends and didn't cost them anything. But Anne, from the start, had realised that they would have to secure accommodation where they could and it would not be free of charge either.

There would be an abundance of coaching inns along The Bath Road, for many people from London visited Bath and as a consequence the roads should be better. She was also aware that a number of the roads were toll roads and payment must be made for the use of them. However there had been numerous occasions when travellers had refused payment considering that it was nothing but extortion and that the money taken in tolls was invariably used for purposes other than the maintenance of the roads they charged for the use of.

There was a generally held belief that roads should be free to use and in the years following the journey, the government had gradually reduced the number of licences granted for toll charges. Anne reflected that they would have saved a deal of money had the journey been undertaken in 1861 and not 1831.

After leaving Kelvedon, the first night was spent at Brentwood; her mother had friends living there and word had been sent to them requesting overnight shelter for the travellers. Brentwood was a place Anne knew quite well and on occasion, they had been known to attend the local Quaker Meeting House; a building which had been used at one time as a bakehouse. In the years gone by there had been a peasant revolt in Brentwood and many were killed; she also remembered the story told amongst Quakers, of William Hunter – a young man of only 19, who was burnt at the stake for refusing to accept the Catholic dogma of transubstantiation; the belief that in the Catholic Mass the bread and the wine became the actual body and blood of Jesus Christ. He was later considered to be a martyr and at the very spot where he was executed an elm tree was planted which was known as The Martyr Elm; Anne and her sisters had been taken to see it when they attended Brentood Meeting House.

London proved to be a great deal busier than Anne had

remembered it and she was indeed most grateful for the presence of George Milligan. Businesses and dwellings were to be found on both banks of The Thames and much trade was generated from ferrying services; there were several bridges but they were often choked with carriages and carters so at the time of this visit another bridge was under construction and due to open later in the year. George told her that it was to be a replacement for the old London Bridge which had become so congested it was difficult to pass along; it would appear that people, for some reason or other, had built houses and business on the bridge – some 200 in number; George considered that half the people who lived in London were crazy and the other half lazy.

Anne enjoyed having George with her – he was good company and very chatty, telling her lots about the places they passed; Isaac was not excluded from their conversation, though he could not see as much as he would have liked to due to his recumbent position in the back of the cart.

At Hyde Park Corner George was leaving them to continue with their journey which now took them on the busy thoroughfare of Knightsbridge, so called said George because of the River Westbourne which the thoroughfare used to cross over. He pointed out that of late the river had been culverted and put into a piping system to run under London.

Isaac was particularly interested in this, wondering if perhaps that had ever been a water mill there.

Hyde Park Corner was also the first place coming out of London where they would have to pay a toll for the use of the turnpike; she couldn't recall how much it was they paid; on the rest of the route to Bath they had paid toll charges at regular intervals. Before leaving them, George gave them details of a place to stay at Hounslow, telling them it was a very popular place for people to stop, change horses and put up for the night.

There was a final warning from George to beware of the dangerous highwaymen, who had been encountered by many of the travellers along the Great West Road on account of the route being used by the wealthy and prosperous en-route for Bath.

Anne had remarked that they wouldn't get wealthy stealing the meagre belongings and cash they were carrying; and they certainly would not find anything in the way of jewellery, her wedding ring being the only item of jewellery she wore.

But they heeded his warning, which included advice not to be on the road after dark; the favourite time for highwaymen and cut-throats – but not exclusively so.

She could not deny it, the roads were very good and well maintained and superior to the roads they had encountered in Norfolk and Suffolk – but of course, for such luxury of travelling they had to pay for each stretch, which would have numbered a dozen or more, before they got to Bath.

Hounslow seemed to be a place dedicated to the traveller and there was no shortage of choice for places to stay. She tried to avoid the obvious taverns and inns, where high levels of drinking could having been taking place and in which Isaac would not have been happy to stay, instead selecting lodgings from the non-licensed establishments.

As Anne closed her eyes that night, she felt as if she and

Isaac were on the other side of a hill; not an actual land mass but the hump of their journey. The next one hundred miles would be anything but free-wheeling but at least they were reasonably certain of getting there; they had enough money to pay the turnpike tolls and the lodgings. When they got to Bath they were assured of a place to stay with some relatives of Abigail; how long that stay would be, she wasn't to know but Abigail had assured her that they would be welcome to stay for as long as it took to get Isaac well again.

She said a silent prayer expressing how grateful to her Lord she would be if he would grant a cure for her husband; this wasn't a rarity for she seemed to be forever saying this prayer in her heart as well as at other times when she and Isaac would be joined in their prayers. She must learn to have more faith – learn to trust in God to bring about a happy conclusion to their endeavours. She needed Isaac to be back in his place; his proper place as head of the family – she needed his strength.

Her misgivings of two days ago now seemed far behind her and she was determined to approach the rest of the journey with a new vigour and Isaac would get better; he would get better.

*C*hapter thirteen

Ann wondered to herself if she would ever have that strength of purpose again; just as she had some thirty years ago. She had lost such a lot in losing Isaac but just as she had then determined to go forward, she must be resolved to be strong again for the family. True, she would not have Isaac at her side but she felt he would be watching over her and the family; and in the fullness of time she would join him but not before she had got James into a fit and healthy state in order to take his place where she knew he belonged, alongside his brothers.

Above anything else he wanted was to be on an equal footing with Francis, Frederick and George; to be making his own contribution to the continued success of the company. Her boys – how she loved them all; and Charles – poor Charles just twenty-one; but it was a blessed relief when he went to his maker; his suffering was over and he had suffered greatly most of his life.

She was quite amazed how the days passed before they moved out of Pension Stafford. It was the twenty fifth day of the year's third month and she was to write in her diary - "Left Menton with a heavy heart – here I had enjoyed much with my beloved husband and here I learned the bitter grief that I would see him no more in this world."

But before that, there was the packing to be done; they had been in Menton nearly five months and apart from the clothes they had brought with them, there were the souvenirs and other goods they had acquired during their stay. Sadly there was nothing to pack for Isaac but there were the things they had collected during his short sojourn at the pension; much of this consisted of seeds they had been given by the kind people who had those magnificent gardens that she would always remember.

She'd suggested to Isaac that they might not fair as well in the East Yorkshire's soil and climate but for his sake she must take them home and give them a chance; it would have meant a lot to Isaac and it would mean a lot to her, if there was some lasting reminder of their last days together; and that reminder being in the form of new life and colour to comfort her.

Also in the final days before the time of departure, other guests had pressed gifts upon them, mostly in the form of books they might enjoy reading.

She had mixed feelings as she clicked the lock on the last of their cases; it was a wonderful place – and there could be no doubt that James had found the health benefits foretold by Doctor Bennett.

As indeed Isaac had done before he made the decision to cut short his restorative vacation with them, to attend to matters in Hull; matters which his other three sons could well have dealt with. OH Isaac – why?

How many times was she going to ask herself this? Would she ever be able to move on from the thought that if he had remained in Menton, continued enjoying the health giving climate which everyone felt some benefit from, he would still be here with them now. But the thought did occur to her that it may well have been his time to be called to his heavenly home; it could have happened here in Menton as well as Hull. Then what would she have done?

He would have to be either buried here or be taken back to Hull for interment. How would she have coped with that? And then what would have been the effect on James? Would he have reacted badly to such an event – maybe he would blame himself for it, due to them being in the south of France for his benefit.

Was this how it was always going to be? Or would there come a time when she would be able to say that everything happens for the best if we trust in God.

There was no doubt about it, the move to a new place on the Riviera would help; they would miss all the new friends they had made but it would be something of a relief not to have the continuous question - "Are you feeling any better today?"

Sometimes she had wanted to scream at them - "I am not ill; I have lost my husband – that is all; I am feeling sad and bereft and I must grieve – I want to be able to grieve. There will be plenty of time for being jolly but not yet."

She never did say any of those things but she could not help but feel it might be good to be able to.

They were going to stay at Genoa for the remainder of their vacation on The Riviera; Doctor Bennett assured them that the climate there would be just as beneficial for James; he also agreed, that under the circumstances, it might be best for them to move on.

They were to share a voiture with the Hunts, Mr & Mrs and their daughter. It would be comfortable enough for the carriage would seat six.

What a pleasant journey it turned out to be – though not a short one – about a hundred miles in total. Conversation was good from all of them and the scenery they passed through was quite breathtaking the landscape abounding with orange and lemon trees only broken up with luxuriant palms. It was a three-day journey visiting Bordighera, San Remo and Oneglia before arriving at Genoa at teatime. Miss Stafford had very kindly arranged for them to stay with a friend of hers, who took only a very small number of guests, until they were ready to return to England. Anne was happy enough about this – though at another time she would have welcomed a larger company of people.

James had his own room and she hers; the views were not as good as they had been at Menton but there were some splendid walks and the whole place was much busier that Menton.

Fellow guests were most agreeable – both of them German but with a very good command of English language. They really do put us English folk to shame, thought Anne; we expect the rest of the world to have a command of our own tongue and yet we don't seem to think it at all necessary to learn their language.

She determined that if ever they came to the Riviera again – she would be reasonably conversant with French; well – as conversant as she could be. Her mother had taught all the girls some basic rudiments of the language but that was a very long time ago and not having any use to speak it up until now, the little she had learned had floated out of her intellect.

For a couple of days she hadn't given her mind to any more recollections; the days were filled with new experiences and meeting new people. James loved Genoa and in many ways, it lifted his spirits as well; the atmosphere was still good for him – good for them both; it was altogether the right thing moving from Menton; she felt, somehow, free of the burden of loss. It was odd how that feeling came upon her, Isaac being gone from her only a few weeks but there was a sense of building a new life for herself – a life that would have to be without him. He did so much for her and saw to all the aspects of their relationship that he considered it was his duty to do as a husband; that wasn't to say he domineered her in any way – though he could at times be quite forceful and yet she knew him to be the gentlest and most considerate of men. Her sons would more than likely want to take over some of that aspect of her life but she must be very careful not to encourage them into thinking that she was helpless. But she was going to miss him terribly – and the thoughts of going home to Hull, in some ways, did not thrill her greatly.

It was the third day of their stay at Genoa, when she found herself alone for a while; James had gone off with one of the guests to see some sight or other and she had taken a slow walk down to the harbour; it amused her that she could still be attracted to water and especially the sea. Being by the sea was something which had remained with her from childhood – the hours she'd spend on the marshes nearby where they lived at Cley Next To The Sea; she was quite sad in a way when they left Cley to live in Kelvedon for that was twenty miles from the nearest sea shore at East and West Mercia.

Genoa certainly was not as relaxed a place as Menton but that day, walking round the harbour, she found a quiet spot where she could sit in the shade and give her mind over to thinking about some more of her young life with Isaac.

Dobbin was taking them down The Great East Road for another twenty miles which brought them to Maidenhead. Travelling was so much easier for them on this road; it was better maintained and constructed which, to a large extent, we have to thank the Romans for. More importantly still it was more comfortable for Isaac and they were getting nearer to their destination each day.

Maidenhead was the first place they had needed to cross the river Thames and they were able to use Maidenhead's new bridge; well – it would always be the "new bridge" to the people of Maidenhead, even though it eventually would replace the old bridge in 1877 and very glad they were of it.

Reading was their next port of call – in which Anne, under different circumstances, would have liked to have spent a few days; it being such an interesting place.

They were to put up at The Crown - which, when staying with her mother, she had written to; it was a pleasant coaching inn on London Street and opposite was Joseph Huntley's bakery; which, though they didn't know it at the time, was to become famous for their biscuits and employed hundreds of people as their own company were to do in Hull.

But when they visited it was just Joseph and his son; they

being members of the Society Of Friends had recommended the Crown as a place to stay. Joseph, a diligent and enterprising business man, used to sell his biscuits to the coach travellers who stopped off at The Crown on their journey to Bath and Bristol. Isaac enjoyed talking to Joseph Huntley – them having something in common in being members of the Society of Friends and both working with flour.

Their journey onwards took them through Newbury, then to Marlborough and Chippenham, arriving at Bath at midday on the thirteenth day of their journey. As they passed the sign on the road announcing that they had arrived at The City Of Bath – she and Isaac almost wept with joy.

"Anne – you are a wonder; how is it that a stubborn obstinate man like me could deserve such a wonderful wife as you?"

Anne smiled at him, "Well there must be some good reason but nothing comes to me just at the moment."

They laughed together; much of their laughter out of relief but Anne knew that though this had been an arduous two weeks – there may yet well be more to come; not maybe so physically arduous but emotionally – and she was not wrong in those feelings.

Chapter fourteen

Ann had never been to Bath, so it was all new to her; under other circumstances it could have been quite exciting – and in a way it still was. But she mustn't lose sight of the fact that this was going to be no holiday; Isaac's needs had to come first – that is not to say she would need to be in attendance night and day and there was a little time for her to see something of the famous city which attracted so many of the rich and influential of the nation.

First things first – they had to find their lodgings which had been arranged for them by Abigail; it was not far from the hospital, to which Ann had written asking if it were possible to bring Isaac for treatment. They'd replied saying that he would be welcome to have free access to the treatment – however, subject to treatment space, they must be prepared to wait a few days or even longer, before the treatment could begin.

Isaac spent a restful night on that first day at Bath – but Ann – though tired, was awake for quite a while before sleep claimed her. All the things that must be done – arrangements made for Isaac's treatment.

She had been assured by the family that they were staying with, that any help they needed would be forthcoming and that was a comfort for her to know; tomorrow she must also get somewhere nice for Dobbin to stay. He would be glad of the rest; they all would but there wasn't to be much rest for her. Contact with Quaker friends meeting house would be another thing she must attend to.

Her sleep that night, when it came, was fitful and when she awoke the next morning she felt she hadn't really slept at all; Jane, their hostess remarked that she looked more tired than she had looked the night before and suggested that she should go back to bed; but Ann assured her that it would be to no avail until she had done what she needed to do – then maybe she would take a nap after lunch.

When they had both breakfasted and Isaac assisted with his washing and dressing, she half carried Isaac into the front room of their lodgings and helped get him comfortable on the day bed by the window. From there he could see out into the street, which was quite a busy thoroughfare, bringing in traffic from Bristol and the West; in truth he would have been glad of someone to talk to and she would have to see about that once she knew more people and about the place. Jane wasn't much in the way of conversation and her husband and son were both occupied during the day at their own jobs, coming home at night too tired to engage in debate.

Much of the talk before they left Boston, was of the fear of the plague coming into our country and Boston, being a port, was very nervous; it was causing havoc in Russia – thousands of people were dying in the streets and there were fears that it wouldn't be long before cholera reached us. Early on in the year the government was putting all ships that arrived at our shores into quarantine. Ann had heard talk of it as she had travelled but thought not to share this information with Isaac because he had enough on his plate without worrying about the plague; all the same – it was very frightening for her in 1831; but the efforts of the government were not successful and by October that year Cholera was wreaking havoc in England.

On the first Sunday in Bath she joined the Quaker gathering at the meeting house in Lower Borough Lane; it was so good to be amongst some new friends and there were many offers of help with the getting of Isaac to the hospital each day; this to be accomplished by means of a stretcher.

He wasn't happy about this – being on view to all and sundry and she could appreciate his feelings. Put in the same position she would have been very distressed at being regarded as an invalid to everyone in the street who looked upon them; but facts must be faced – Isaac was an invalid – and he eventually had to come to terms with that. Stretchers bearing people at various levels of treatment were not an uncommon sight in Bath; nor were the beggars, who the city fathers tried to control, without a great deal of success.

Beggars were a fact of life in most towns and cities; she knew some were charlatans of course but for others it was their only means of support; the sight of so many in one place moved Isaac greatly, giving forth to him expressing himself in not undisguised terms about the way the government treated the poor. This drew several haughty looks and not a few "Tuts" from the people who passed by

Ann felt, that in some ways, the sight of these poor wretched people made him more determined to get himself well in order to do something about it.

They had been warned to be careful of the beggars, a serious number of whom were thought to be in league with pickpockets; one distracted the unwitting passer-by whilst the other, light-fingered accomplice, relieved them of their valuables. Many of the visitors who came to stay in Bath were from the fashionable and wealthy echelons of society and tended to be inclined to display their wealth about their person which made them easy pickings for the riff-raff.

Ann was thankful that her own upbringing had never been such as to encourage her or her sisters, in the way of a showy appearance; in truth, such manner of dress was firmly discouraged by their mother and grandmother, however – a quality garment would always have been preferred to a cheaply made one but restraint would be favoured in the way of embellishments.

But here in Bath – there was every conceivable mode of dress imaginable, with the accent very much on ostentation; particularly in their choice of hats and wigs. She had to admit to herself that these over-the-top dresses were quite a source of entertainment in themselves, not to mention the way the wearers walked; though how some managed to walk being so tied up in corsets and body-shapers, was a mystery all on it's own. But walk they did – on all the fashionable streets and in the parks and gardens; they seemed to be spending half the day walking – or putting it more aptly parading before a gawping, but in many cases, admiring public.

When they weren't walking they were sitting in the coffee houses and the salons frequented by the wealthy. Some did manage to find the time to attend at The Roman Baths or the pump house where they partook of the waters; Ann tried the waters but they were not to her taste – in fact she found them quite vile, as did others but then it had always been supposed that the worst tasting medicine always did you the best good; or so grown-ups used to tell them – as indeed she did with her own children.

Being the kind of place it was, there was evidence everywhere you looked of some miracle cure or other; though the city fathers frowned on the street corner quack-doctors they couldn't be watched all the time and it wasn't difficult to draw a curious crowd from amongst the more health conscious of those walking about the place.

But of one thing Ann was certain, this city was a truly amazing place; its architecture was quite something to behold; the corporation buildings like palaces – even the dwelling houses of the townspeople had been built with the accent on grandeur.

Churches and such like establishments nearly always were built to give the impression of a deep devotion to God but Ann knew from her own experience that the devotion, in the main, was to be symbols of the wealth of their benefactors. Quaker meeting houses would never set out to compete with the established churches, opting for the rather more plain construction.

Much of the objection that Quakers had towards the established church was the display of magnificence it seemed to find necessary both inside and outside of their buildings; this coupled with a sense of flamboyance evident in the mode of worship and the attire of the ministers in the church, was found by most Quakers to be whole unacceptable.

At one time there was much antagonism towards Quakers, who were considered by the established church to be best dissenters and at worst, heretics, to the point that burials in establishment cemeteries was forbidden to them, it being consecrated ground and so Quakers had to provide their own graveyards.

A shiver went through her – even in the high temperatures they were experiencing in Genoa, there was the cold hard fact that Isaac would also now have been buried in a Quaker grave.

Chapter fifteen

How many days had they been in Genoa? She couldn't think; three four or was it just two? She seemed to have been whisked about here and there to see this particular garden or that lovely church.

In truth she hadn't taken a lot of it in but James was enjoying himself so much she was happy to go along on the excursions if only for his sake. He was a different man altogether from the one who had set out for The South of France almost five months ago.

Sometimes she would watch him chatting to this person or that and an immense feeling of joy would surge through her, knowing how much suffering he'd had in his young life; if only this improvement in health would last and allow him to lead the full life his older brothers did.

Now and again he would catch her looking at him and say something like, "Have I got a smut on my nose mother?"

She would smile and say - "The biggest smut you ever did see." and they would both laugh.

He was such a thoughtful son; she felt he must have known full well what she was experiencing at those moments but he never demanded to know what she was thinking or chided her in any way for spending so much time in the past and for that she was grateful. Now and again she would share some of her thoughts with him; mention to him a particular event or incident which had taken place on their journey and which had come to mind; James would be genuinely interested in the things she had remembered but he didn't press her to reveal her innermost thoughts to him.

Of course, James wasn't born when she had taken Isaac on that long, long journey to get him cured; but when she thought about it – the journey wasn't as long in distance, as they had made to seek a cure of her son's condition. Dobbin would not have made it all this way but he was equal to their mission of thirty years ago; she had a lot to thank Dobbin for – he was indeed the most faithful servant they had ever had. But once they arrived in Bath he could have a well earned rest; a rest which, along with other horses who were in the same situation, he spent on a farm just outside the city; horses of all shapes and sizes and from all backgrounds who had each, in their individual shafts, pulled their various wagon loads and now would not be needed for a few weeks.

When she had taken him to have his break there, he looked quite small amongst some of the other animals and he was certainly not in their class when it came to breed and pedigree; but for her he was by far, quite the most valued of them all. He was such a lovely chap with an easy and unflappable temperament – always willing to go the extra mile for her; she had grown quite fond of him and was, indeed, quite sad when they had to give him back on their return to Boston.

They had been in Bath several weeks, when word came to them at their lodgings, that there was a place for Isaac to have his treatment. Dozens of people had assured them that he would be well in no time; this was her most fervent prayer and though she had great faith in her God – she was also aware that we didn't always get the things we wanted. For both her and Isaac, the whole matter would be in God's hands – he would know what was to be best for them and that was how they were going to have to leave it.

For the duration of his treatment – however long that might be – Isaac would have to stay in the hospital; she could visit him and bring him food but for the most part he would have to remain under their care. At the time she thought it was going to be strange not having Isaac by her side and to a certain extent she had misgivings; she had always been there for him – night and day. There to comfort him and to hold him close to her in the times of despair; and there had been many – mostly brought on by the pain he was going through.

Apart from the physical pain he also continued to worry himself about the mill and how his brother was managing without him; typical of Isaac – hadn't the same thing been the case just a few months ago. His mind couldn't settle; the business again – took him away from her and the result most surely was his untimely death.

When Isaac did go into hospital, it wasn't quite so distressing for her as she imagined it would be; yes she missed the closeness of him during the night and for a few days her sleep was disturbed but gradually it became easier for her.

They'd been told that the treatment could last for five to six weeks; she wondered what was she going to do with all that time to herself. True – some of the day was spent in visiting him after his daily treatment, which consisted of him being immersed up to his neck in the healing spa water for five hours at a time; only his head could remain out of the bath.

Conversation wasn'tencouraged and patients were advised relax as much as was possible; Isaac had, at first found that wasn't easily practised but became used to the warm, soothing atmosphere which existed in the treatment areas and soon he was lying there quite happily.

Despite Isaac's previous misgivings he was now becoming convinced that the treatment was having it's declared beneficial effect; he was able to move his limbs more freely and without too much pain. With some help he was soon able to walk a few steps and this increased his confidence greatly; but there were also days when things weren't so good – and the pain would once again return. This, they were told, was always going to be possible and must be considered to be part of the healing process.

Ann took full advantage of making excursions into the city and the villages roundabout and enjoyed the walks she made; she was a welcome member of the Quaker community and founded many new friendships, all of them wanting to give them their support. Some would visit Isaac when he had completed his daily treatment and this Isaac welcomed, being fond of good stimulating conversation – though she had to make them aware that he was not to become too excited. With Isaac this was easier said than done, for such was part of his personality, oft-times indulging himself in times of immoderate argument; particularly about this or that decision made by the government or some new bill that had been passed.

Isaac was a passionate opponent to anything that, to his

mind, smacked of injustice and when the matter came into question, was not afraid to voice his thoughts on the subject

Sometimes she wished he would keep his opinions to himself – particularly when the doctors came to see him but for the most part she felt that the majority of them accepted that it was part of his character.

When she visited him he would want to know what she had been doing and where she had been; she knew that many another wife would have raised some objection to having to relay, to her husband, the doings of the day but she didn't mind; in fact she joyed in sharing her experiences with him – which for the most part made him happy. She was careful not to introduce things into the conversation that would elicit his disapproval; certainly – some of the goings on in the city cafés would have offended his principals and so she didn't tell him about them.

Life went on from day to day – and as the days went by, on the whole, he was getting better and better; she was expecting at any time his impatience would manifest itself – and it did; once he was walking unaided – he wanted to be off and couldn't understand why he should still undergo further daily immersions.

She recalled the times without number she had encouraged him to take the doctor's advice; most of the time it worked, though sometimes he became so irritated that he could not be pacified.

But praise the Lord – the day came; the day when the doctors declared themselves satisfied with his condition and his treatment completed.

At the time of their departure Isaac was given strict instructions about how he should look after himself, if he was to benefit fully from the treatment he had been given; quite a long list of advice on the "dos and don'ts" which she fervently hoped that Isaac would follow.

One piece of advice that didn't go down well at all with Isaac was that, due to the damp fenland areas being notorious for bringing on suffering to those who might be prone to rheumatism, they should consider living in a different part of the country.

This didn't go down well at all with Isaac – who felt it was unreasonable that they should advocate such measures. His work and his livelihood, he insisted, were bound up in living and working in that part of the country; it was not going to be possible for him to take any other course for the foreseeable future, than to continue working and living there; and that he considered was final.

But what he didn't know at the time, was that circumstances beyond his control were even now being experienced back in Boston; circumstances which would necessitate rethinking his position.

In short Isaac was to discover that, in the comparatively short time he had been away – all was not well.

Chapter sixteen

Their departure from Bath had with it, for Anne, mixed feelings; yes – she was glad that Isaac was well again – and yes she would be glad to see her children again but after the little town of Boston, the city of Bath had been quite an experience for her. Although she wasn't in the least drawn to emulate the fashionable ladies seen out walking about almost everywhere you looked, she could not help but be impressed by the splendour of it all.

The architecture – the gardens – the people, were all very different to what she had been used to; Oh – Boston had it's fine buildings and St. Botolph's Church, which was known locally as "The Stump", which drew the sightseers from miles away. It was reputed to be one of the biggest parish churches in Britain; and general opinion was that, up to recent times, the church had the highest roof of any building in the World.

It would be wonderful to be in her own house and her own kitchen again; laughingly she thought to herself that she would have to re-establish her territory in the kitchen – that was if her daughter Elizabeth would let her. Yes – of course she would but there wasn't a shadow of doubt in Ann's mind that her dearest Bessie would have ruled the roost in the house whilst they had been away.

She hoped the boys hadn't given her too much aggravation; not that any of that would have come from Charles – such a

mild mannered child and a very gentle character in manhood –
which he had only just attained before he was taken from her.

It had been decided that Isaac would take the reins for the
journey back to Boston and though they would still go through
London, they would take a shorter route back to Boston, which
would miss out Kelvedon. Her mother would understand their
eagerness to be back with their own children again; it had
been over two months since they had left Boston and such a
lot had happened to them in that time. Ann always felt
afterwards that Bath was a definite turning point in their lives
and someday she'd like to go back and visit the place; maybe
now she would do just that – in memory of Isaac, who had
always considered that at Somerset's famous spa many
blessings had been showered upon them.

When they'd gone to collect Dobbin he was at the other side
of the field sharing a hay breakfast with another horse; the
owner of the field told Ann that the two horses had become
great pals over the past few weeks and were always seen
together but when Dobbin saw Ann – he came trotting across
the field to them; his pal followed at a distance and came to a
stop a little way off and Dobbin turned his head to look at him.

Ann had thought to herself – if horses could talk, these two
might be saying quite a lot at that moment; but anyway – he
seemed pleased to see her – and more so when she gave him
a few lumps of sugar.

As he was placed into the shafts of the cart, she felt a touch
sad for him in a way; but come what may, once again he must
be set to work and get them back to Boston. Then sadly, along
with the cart, they would have to get him back to his owners.

After they had collected, from their lodgings, their belongings, which had now been added to by the gifts they had been given by their new Quaker friends, they were on their way.

Once more The Great East Road opened up to them to take them eventually to London; it seemed to Anne, that with Isaac at the wheel the places just whizzed past but in effect, he wasn't taking them that fast at all; fast as it may seem, they were still being overtaken by carriages wanting to get along at higher speed.

For the most part they didn't engage themselves in much conversation, Isaac being intent on the road and keeping a careful eye on Dobbin, making sure that he wasn't getting overtired and had sufficient breaks for feeding, water and rest.

It was a good feeling to have Isaac back to his normal self and in charge of things; the place where he liked to be. Oh – he wasn't a bully or anything anywhere near it but his illness had brought him so low that he almost handed everything over to her.

But now – he was the old Isaac again; his confidence had been regained and there wasn't anything that he would not be able to do. Bless him – how she loved this man.

Once they hit London Isaac began to be more expansive; maybe it was the atmosphere of the capital that gave him the feeling of a new self. They lodged for the night at a reasonably priced establishment near Smithfield Market and which seemed to mostly cater for travellers; it didn't give the impression that it would be rowdy at night – and it wasn't.

It was that night that Isaac really opened up to her about what he had been feeling about himself. How he had thought that he was never going to be anything other than an invalid ever again; partly resigned to being dependant on her for the rest of his life. He also confessed to feelings that it might be better for her if he had been taken to his maker and then she could marry someone who would be a better husband to her.

It had almost broken her heart to hear him saying those words; she had known that his illness had made him feel wretched; made him feel hopeless but she had never thought he was so unhappy about himself.

As they lay there on that warm summer night she felt something inside her saying that come what may – Isaac would be the only man for her; and she told him so.

"Ann – I have said to you many times that I consider myself to be the most fortunate of men and I count myself privileged that you agreed to have me for a husband and no matter whatever may happen in our life together, it will be all the richer for you being by my side."

"Thank you Isaac." was all that she could say without dissolving into tears; but she could feel them welling up inside her – maybe it had been coming for a long time – but before she knew it she was in his arms and the tears flowed.

Isaac stroked her hair and whispered - "Oh my dearest Ann it's been pretty rough for you but from now on things are going to get better – you'll see. As I said before – this has been a turning point in our lives; your strength has kept me going and brought me through this time of despair and for that I shall be in your debt till the day I die."

Those words went again through her mind and she was so lost in that scene that she hadn't noticed that James was standing beside her.

"Is everything alright mother?"

"James – I hadn't noticed you there."

"Lost in your thoughts again."

"Yes James – lost in my thoughts again; was I meant to be doing something?"

"Not if you don't wish it mother but we did think we might go out for a ride to the St Lorenzo Cathedral; some other people are going to make a visit there and there is a space for us in the landau; we are invited to join them – that's if you'd like to."

"I would be happy to join them James; I feel I've been neglecting you somewhat – I hope you'll forgive me."

"Mother – you don't need to be forgiven; you must just take things a day at a time – it's only natural that you'll be wanting to spend time with your thoughts." "Your father was a good man James."

"I am aware of that mother."

"Sometimes I wonder to myself just what I'm going to do without him; he meant so much to me – I could say he was the biggest part of my life. So many things we shared together James – and now we'll never share anything again."

"But you have your memories mother."

"Yes – I have my memories."

"What's more – you'll have more life to call upon to create new memories; father would have wanted that."

They were silent for a few moments – James not wanting to intrude further on her thoughts – then quite suddenly she turned to him.

"Well – what are we waiting for – let us away to see Genoa's great cathedral."

It was a fairly cloudy day – not the sort of day when rain would descend upon them – just cloudy; but thankfully cooler. Some of the nights had been quite unbearably hot and there was hardly a breath of air; but those nights, thankfully, didn't come too often. In the full summer it could well have been very unpleasant indeed.

Their six months stay would soon be up and then they would return to Hull and the English Spring – well late Spring; they should be back by the end of April – which was just a few weeks away.

They were very pleasant people, with whom, they joined up with their trip to the cathedral; they also had brought their young son to The Riviera for the climate cure. He was considerably younger than James but James had taken it upon himself to be a big brother to him, which his parents appreciated.

Upon arrival at The Saint Lorenzo Cathedral they were advised to go carefully as much of it was under restoration; in fact it had been under restoration for nearly three hundred years. But the cathedral authorities were quite convinced that restoration work would be complete by the end of the century; but there were others who confided in them that this had been the projection for the two previous centuries.

Nevertheless, it was an impressive building and well supported by the people of Genoa; Ann could admire the painting and the sculptures, clearly the work of some truly talented artisans – and no doubt much appreciated by those who worshipped there. For herself and her places of worship, she much preferred the quietness and simplicity of the Quaker meeting houses but she could not fail to be impressed by the efforts of great men.

After an hour of walking about Ann excused herself, begging to be allowed to sit for a while in the piazza outside the front of the cathedral; though not large, it was a pleasant piece of space which attracted tourists and musicians; she had a wide variety of tastes in music and that provided by these players was of a most restful kind. She was happy to sit and enjoy the music but in no time at all she was back on their return journey from Bath; the place of cure and restoration. She wondered to herself just how many folk had arrived as invalids and after treatment had gone back to their homes pain free.

Although Isaac had had his reservations, he had fallen into the treatment routine quite readily but the one thing he had groused about was the food. He had remarked that it may well have sustained the body but did very little for the spirit. Ann had felt quite guilty when she was made aware of the meals he was given and been sorely tempted on her daily visits to the hospital to sneak in a little treat for him but the nurses and doctors were on the look-out for things being brought in. As they stressed to all the patients – the diet was as much part of their treatment as everything else.

Sometimes when she visited him she was invited to help with his daily routines; as she had pointed out to the staff – she had lifted him on and off the cart each night of the journey from Boston, so lifting him into his daily treatment bath presented very little difficulty for her. Poor Isaac sitting in the water for 5 hours a day – with just his head poking through the steaming surface. It was very tempting to giggle but she knew she must not for Isaac's sake but all the same he was a comical sight; and the smell – it was anything but pleasant; still – if it was doing its work – what did an unpleasant smell matter?

After a few weeks of the treatment she was allowed to take him out for a few hours each day; for this she hired a Bath Chair, in which she could push him along – at first he'd protested but then he realised that it was going to be the only way she could move him around the city.

When she did take him out he was required to wear a metal badge fastened to his coat to say that he was a patient at 'The Min' which was the nickname the locals gave to the Mineral Water Hospital.

At first, Isaac was quite chagrined at this requirement, the main purpose of wearing the badge being to alert publicans as to who they were and thus refuse to serve them any alcoholic beverages. Isaac had pointed out to the nurses that it was not his practice to even go into public houses let alone drink in one. But he had to still wear the badge all the same on the basis of the fact that it was one rule for all and there could be no exceptions – that is if he wanted to leave the hospital premises.

Parade Gardens, down by the River Avon, was their favourite place; the floral displays were so beautiful and very well kept. This was Isaac's delight – being amongst the flowers he was never happier. Often a band would be playing on the rather elaborate bandstand and they could sit awhile and enjoy the music. Sometimes as a special treat they would have tea and buns which were served on payment of a small amount; Bath buns of course – the speciality of all the bakers of Bath – each with their own individual claim to be the very best. Basically they were a sweet roll made from a milk-based yeast dough, with a lump of sugar baked in the bottom and after baking more crushed sugar sprinkled on top. They might contain candied fruit, currants, raisins or sultanas. But without a doubt they were delicious and probably very bad for them.

How he had loved those excursions when he could get out of the hospital; out into the fresh air for a change. At the hospital there was a permanent smell of sulphur and bleach, with disinfectant added to it but out in Parade Gardens it was quite splendid. Sometimes the river was fast flowing; that was when it had been raining – sometimes it was still and hardly any flow at all.

Of course, Ann and Isaac had been used to a river flowing through the town; back home in Boston – the River Witham came in and out with the tide, bringing into the port ships from many far away ports. There were no boats or barges as such on this part of the River Avon – instead they would travel down the Avon and Kennet canal down to The Pulteney Weir, which banked up the water to drive the mills. Isaac was very much impressed by all this; as indeed he was by many things. His body may have been disabled but his mind was as sharp as a razor. Always thinking up something new – that was her Isaac; new dreams to dream almost every day.

London left behind them, they were now on The Great North Road – only a hundred miles to Grantham – then another thirty to Boston and home. Home – it couldn't come soon enough for

Ann; how she would hug the children and tell them all about their adventure. They would be kept going for weeks with tales of the things she had discovered and they would listen eagerly – especially Charles, who, though the quietest of them all showed great interest in all things. Bessie would want to know how everyone behaved and what they wore; Francis and George would want to know the minutest details about everything they had done or seen.

Would she be truly glad to see Boston again – that was the question; would she be happy to settle back again into the rhythm of the life they had lived such a short time ago? Although living in Boston had brought her great happiness as wife and mother, it had also been where she had experienced some of the greatest anxiety and worry; where she had seen her beloved Isaac slowly decline in health; seen the young man she had fallen in love with turn into the man he became. Though he was now transformed to his earlier self again, the fears that everything could revert to the way it used to be; back to his being plagued with the pestilential rheumatic condition – back to distress and irritability. What the doctors had said about the climatic conditions of the The Fen Country and the widely acknowledged physical agues of the folk who lived there – she would not be able to remove from her mind. Oh yes – Isaac is cured; is free of pain and discomfort – capable of walking about like other men – doing his work but how long will it last if he is subjected to the previous lifestyle and the damp atmosphere ever present all around them? He couldn't live indoors all the time; couldn't be kept by the side of the kitchen fire for ever. It could well be that she would have to get Isaac to give some very serious thought and consideration for their circumstances; this was going to be no easy task – the memory of his sufferings would be short, now that he was restored to good health.

Isaac seemed to be of an easier frame of mind leaving London and once driving along Ermine Street, the old name of The Great North Road, built by the Roman invaders. Sitting there beside him her mind drifted to the name Ermine Street and she pondered to herself about how such a name came about.

"Isaac – why was The Great North Road called Ermine Street?"

Isaac smiled at her; as he had told her many times, she was indeed a woman amongst women.

"Dearest Ann – how many other women would be bothered about what a road was called? How many female minds would ponder such things?"

But Ann was different – she knew that he'd known that from the very start; from the day they had first met at The Quaker Meeting House in Woodbridge and he had told her so.

At their first meeting, when many another woman would have wanted to chat about family matters, Ann wanted to know how The Corn Laws affected Lincolnshire and the milling business; she knew that it was self evident everywhere how the much hated laws affected the ordinary people's lives; how the bread – a major part of their staple diet was becoming too costly for them to buy and families were going hungry and she had wondered what it was like in Lincolnshire.

Isaac had told her that her enquiring mind had drawn him to

her and coupled with the fact that she was a fine looking girl made his desire to make her his wife was made more earnest. Ann was pleased that he had regarded her in that way – though she was equally sure that there must have been times when he would have much preferred her to be, not quite so concerned with the issues of the day. But one thing was certain, she never neglected him or his family and she had made him the main concern of her life; a thing she was aware that most wives professed to do but in fact the truth often was their position in society – as well as the s tatus of each of their husbands, which was paramount in their lives.

So she was sitting next to her man on a borrowed horse and cart; so much for status – but she was happy and content; more so now that he was well again and her most earnest prayer was that he would remain so. But much was going to depend on a change in their lives; a change she knew he would kick against and she had to face the fact that she was going to have to be very strong.

Chapter seventeen

They were now ten miles out of London and that little bit nearer home. Isaac turned to look at her and she knew the look – it was saying that he was going to come out with something quite profound.

She was right,"You've got to hand it to the Romans; they certainly knew how to build roads. Very clever people."

"Oh yes I'll agree with that – but what they believed in wasn't clever at all."

"Now then Ann – what they believed in they believed in fervently, which is more than can be said for some people who claim our belief; and some Romans did convert to Christianity."

"But, as a nation, it took more than three hundred years for them to realise that Christianity held much more for them than their pagan gods."

"Yes – you're quite right Ann – but long before that they built the road that we're now using and if we follow our noses we could go all the way to York – with a branch off to Lincoln; course it's not the same road – it's been added to but it was them – with or without Christianity, who had the vision to build it."

He was very knowledgeable was her Isaac; strangely enough they had both been to the same school – Ackworth in Pontefract; not both at the same time of course and it was a long time later when they met. She hadn't liked it at all and had run away; what had she been thinking about? Ackworth was thought to be an excellent Quaker school – and countless successful people owed their good education to the establishment but she hadn't liked being away from home. She hadn't missed out on learning though – none of them had; her mother was her teacher and her mother's school for Quaker girls, which had been set up after they moved to Kelvedon, being small by comparison with Ackworth, was well respected around those parts.

But the fact remained – to her it always seemed to be a cold establishment – and Pontefract was a very far cry from Menton. How strange that Ackworth should come to her mind; but maybe not so strange at all – didn't she lose her lovely Constance there; yes dearest Constance took ill and died there – she'd hardly completed a term when she was tragically taken from them; poor James had suffered in the loss so very deeply – them both being born close together. In many ways he felt that he should have been able to do something to prevent the tragedy; felt that he should have been her protector.

The school hadn't much appealed to James before Constance had died but afterwards Ackworth was not a happy place for him and eventually he was to come home before his education had been completed but it had given him a valuable foundation; prior to Ackworth he had attended Packer's Academy during their stay in Nottingham.

But that was much later in their lives – there was still a great deal to cover in Boston – but memory was never a strictly tidy thing; who had said that to her – perhaps it was grandma Kinsey – she often came out with such sayings.

Isaac was certainly right about the road; the great highway to The North with new places along the route, many of which she had never heard of, much less visited.

Although she knew that Isaac was keen to be back home and back home as soon as possible, they had to be aware of how much they could expect Dobbin to do in a short space of time; he'd had such a long break from doing anything really tasking; nothing more strenuous than galloping across the field with his newly made chum; she had taken him out for rides now and then – several of them to Twerton, where her friend Abigail and her husband had lived prior to them setting up home in Boston.

It was only a couple of miles from Bath and in truth she could quite easily have walked the short distance but it seemed a good opportunity to give Dobbin some exercise. On her behalf, Abigail had contacted some family friends who still lived there; telling them about her and Isaac. They had even been offered the chance to lodge in Twerton but she felt it would be intruding on the good nature of people she had never met. It was on the other side of Twerton where most of the family lived and were involved in milling themselves; the particular mill being water driven by Newton Brook, which led itself winding and twisting down to the River Trent. A little bridge had to be crossed to get to the mill; a bridge with a most unusual name – it had always made her smile when she thought of it.

"Isaac – do you remember that little bridge we had to cross

when we visited Newton mill at Twerton." "Twerton, mother?"
But it wasn't Isaac who was with her – it was James; she had
been so lost in her memories and somehow connected James,
now taking a seat beside her in cathedral piazza, with Isaac.

"Oh James" she chuckled, "I was talking to your father."
James smiled at her – she could see many things in that
smile; certainly there was love there but the smile contained
concern as well.

"It's quite all right James – I'm not going mad."

"Of course not mother."

"I was thinking aloud; the image was so vivid – I was lost in it
– then you were suddenly sitting beside me, as your father
had done when we were riding on that cart with Dobbin out in
front and ...."

There she stopped, turned to James and patted his hand,
"I expect you want to be off."

"No hurry mother – not for a while yet; it could be another
hour before we need to be away. I left our friends in the
cathedral to come and to see if you were alright."

"Making sure I hadn't been whisked off by the gypsy
musicians? They look so carefree – just happy to play their
music and sing their songs for the coppers that people put
onto the plates they hold out."

"Maybe you wanted to join them in their singing."

"Oh no James – they wouldn't have got many coppers
then more likely they would have had buckets of water thrown
at them – me included."

"But mother – you have a lovely singing voice."

"You're very kind James – but I know my limitations."

"So – where was this place Twerton and the bridge you were asking about?"

"Somerset – and it was a very long time ago; it was a Bridge over a stream, which supplied the water to drive the mill I used to visit; sometimes your father came as well. It was the time we were staying in Bath."

"When he was having his treatment?"

"Yes – that was the time; there wasn't a lot for me to do when your father was having the therapy – he would be immersed in the spring water for five or six hours at a time. I'd sometimes sit and read to him but you know your father; he would tell me I ought to be getting out in the fresh air not sitting in the sulphur laden atmosphere of the remedial baths."

"Sounds pretty grim to me."

"It was James – but it was doing it's stuff; getting him better so having to put up with the effluvium seemed like a small price to pay. Sometimes he would be glad to see me but sometimes he wanted to be alone; so I took trips out and about – and when he was well enough and they let him out of the hospital for a few hours – he would come with me."

"The bridge mother?"

"Yes – the bridge – oh why can't I remember its name? Such an unusual name – and it always made me chuckle."

"But now you can't remember it."

"No I can't remember it – and it will bother me all day if I don't – so if at some point I blurt out a funny word – you'll know what it is."

They both had laughed and were still laughing when their fellow guests arrived; James and Ann were laughing so much

155

that the others joined in.

"We don't know what we are laughing at – but you and James are finding something so funny that we've caught your mirth."

There were times such as this when she saw Doctor Bennett she felt an urge to run up to him and give him a hug; most of the time he was to be found in Menton but from time to time he would make visits to Genoa – to see how his "patients" were getting along.

When last he had seen James he had joked with him about being a very eligible bachelor and imagined that he would have many young ladies "setting their caps at him". James had been quite amused at the good doctor's expression but to her knowledge there were at least three who had taken a shine to her son. But in his own time, he would make known his intention to take a wife.

Privately he had made known to her that his illness held him back from entering into marriage feeling that due to his bouts of ill-health it would not be right take a wife. She couldn't argue with this decision but nevertheless when it came it would be a happy time for all of them.

As had been arranged and spot on time, their landau arrived to take them back to the pension; quite a short distance but he would take them the long way round the better to see all that was to be seen of the city and the surrounding areas.

Their driver was quite knowledgeable about the history and the politics of the region, which had had its share of upheaval over the years. It was only as recent as March of 1861 that the Sardinian Parliament had passed a law making Sardinia part of The Kingdom Of Italy. So Genoa, which for a time was under French rule, now was governed by Italy; General Garibaldi was the great hero who, a year previously, had led a thousand men from Genoa to win the region back from the French. Thankfully everything was now quite settled and according to the driver was happy being part of Italy.

They were only a few minutes drive away from their final destination when Ann suddenly remembered the name of the bridge. In truth she had been pondering on the matter for a considerable amount of the time during their journey home.

"Pennyquick!" she suddenly blurted out, "Pennyquick Bridge!" Their driver turned to look at her, "Oui – I go quick if you wish it."

This was too much for Ann – what with the driver's face and what he'd said – she just could not contain the laughter. When she'd composed herself she was able to satisfy all of their curiosities, including the drivers who gave a shrug and said
"Anglaise!".

"It seems a very comical name for a bridge mother!"

"That's what we thought!"

"Why should it be called Pennyquick Bridge?

"It was all to do with the farmlands nearby some of which were fields kept as meadow lands for cattle to graze upon. The meadows were hedged with quickthorn to keep the cattle contained."

"Well – that accounts for the quick part of the name but what about the penny?"

"It was good grazing land being well supplied with water and very lush – so much so that the farmer would charge a penny per beast to any who wanted to graze their cattle there; this would mainly be the drovers who brought the cattle to market and needed somewhere for them to feed overnight."

"The drovers wouldn't want the cattle to look hungry when they were taken to market – so I expect it was worth a penny."

"So – Pennyquick meadow gave way to Pennyquick Hill and Pennyquick Bridge."

"That's what grandfather Reckitt used to do in Wainfleet – so father told me."

"That's quite right James – he was a grazier but in his case it was mainly sheep which were brought for grazing."

As they stepped out of the landau at their lodgings Ann offered an apology to their fellow passengers and the driver for her outburst. They wouldn't hear of it, saying that they found the story quite interesting and also amusing. Furthermore it had made a bright end to a most enjoyable day. They had met up with so many agreeable people over their sojourn on The Riviera and in some ways she would have been happy to delay their departure; she might have pressed for them to prolong their stay if it had not been for The Great International Exhibition, which James would have wanted to be home for even if his cure had not been so complete.

There wasn't much time before dinner for her to do anything but get herself ready but when she went back to her room she would spend a little more time with her memories.

They had crammed so much into their lives – so much had happened to change its course from this way to that way; so many turning points – some greater than others but each one of them significant in their own ways.

But now she must give herself more to being on the sidelines – Isaac being gone; in her day to day existence she would find herself becoming more of an observer. She would still have her family around her but without Isaac's lively interest in the business and sharing everything with her she imagined that life would be considerably different. Maybe as more grandchildren came along she would find herself in the role of grandmother – having the young ones stay with her from time to time; not that they weren't welcome when Isaac was alive.

Quite suddenly she felt a heavy wave of tiredness come over her – and almost wished she hadn't to get herself down to the dining room; she could have quite happily taken a nap – perhaps she would – just for ten minutes it would liven her up and as she sat in one of the big arm chairs in her room she just let herself drift away.

Chapter eighteen

She was glad that James had made some new companions; for herself she was happy to sit quietly in her room – but she felt that for his sake she had to show herself and it made James happy. It was a difficult and disturbing time for her and she penned in the journal she kept up during their stay on the Riviera;

"Nothing seems to have any charm for me now; I had hoped to see these places with my dear beloved; I wish only to be useful to my family and prepare myself for a blessed reunion with him some day. How such bereavements loosen the love of life and earthly enjoyments."

But she would not reveal her deepest thoughts to James – maybe some day when she was long gone – he would read her journals but not until then; they were her own private thoughts – she must keep face and show to the family that she was coping with her grief. True – had her mother been here – or her sisters close at hand then conversations with them would bring forth some of her deep feelings and unhappiness. But conversely, she mustn't give the impression that she was unaffected by Isaac's passing – then again, on the other hand, she didn't want the family to think that she needed mollycoddling; oh – it was all so bewildering – nothing ever prepares us for the loss of one on whom you felt that your very existence depended. She supposed that her mother would have said that she must keep herself busy and not dwell too much on the past, as she had done when her own dear father had died; she knew that would have been good advice – but memories were a great comfort to her.

All the same – she would have been glad if James had not been so determined to include her in almost everything. Bless him – he was a wonderful son – so thoughtful and considerate. He was doing what he was doing because he thought it was for the best and that was just fine.

There wasn't much longer to go and they would be on their way home; she knew James wanted to visit La Spezia and then go on up to Pisa to see it's amazing tower – but the thoughts of being home were uppermost in her mind. Just like she'd longed to be home after their stay in Bath

There was only just enough time to get herself ready for dinner. As this was an English run hotel, the general custom was to change for dinner but there wasn't time; she would have to make her day frock suffice; it wasn't very different from most of the clothes she had brought with her anyway – and a quick splash of her hands and face with some of the water from the big china bowl would deal with that part when getting ready to take her meal; a quick comb of her hair, tucking in the wisps and straggles which had come loose from her bun – yes that would do nicely; she now felt tolerably presentable.

Ann counted herself very fortunate that she hadn't adopted the fashion habits of some of the women of the day who were very fond of frills and flounces; applications of powder and rouge; quite shockingly, there were those of her sex who even stooped to painting beauty spots onto their faces; beauty spots indeed – ugly spots more like; dressing for dinner, for those ladies, was a great affair and much of the apparel with which they attired themselves would not have disgraced a banquet at Buckingham Palace.

Seated on one of the quite elaborate chairs in her room, she looked at herself in the ornate dressing table mirror – a thing she was not in a great habit of doing and it passed through her mind, that from the features which now looked back at her, life had not dealt too badly with Ann Reckitt née Colby and the Lord had blessed her with a natural countenance that was not unpleasant; at sixty six – she wasn't doing too badly at all; she had known many women, whom at that age looked quite old – showing greatly lined and wrinkled faces – but not so her. Tut tut, Ann – such thoughts – what would grandmother say? Something very much to the point she shouldn't wonder – and it would have held something about vanity.

But she mustn't delude herself; it was indeed, a quite different reflection to the one she would have seen as a young woman of thirty five, seated next to her beloved Isaac on the low-loading cart being now pulled by their faithful Dobbin along The Great North Road.

Isaac was happy to say that they made very good time, without asking too much of their sturdy cob and within a few days were well on their way to their ultimate destination – home. An abundance of coaches and traps, travelling at great speeds, making their way to York, passed them as they travelled along the well-used highway at their own pace; the much bandied about boast of the coach operators and their passengers being that they could make York in twenty hours. Well, that was as maybe, for themselves they were quite content to make the distance in a considerably greater time scale, at a considerably lesser speed; this as Isaac declared was in order to get their transport, their horse and themselves back to Boston in one piece.

There was much to see and comment on as they travelled along, both Ann and Isaac taking in as much as possible in order to relate their experiences to the children when the arrived back in Boston; because one thing was for sure they would want to know every little detail – bless them.

Baldock was one of the overnight stops, being recommended for a large Quaker contingency there but when they arrived they found that the community of friends was much depleted. Biggleswade was another destination they might have made an attempt to make for but were told, by travellers along the road, that the place had not yet properly recovered from the great fire of 1785 which had destroyed a third of the houses and businesses in the place; that terrible fire, it would appear, had started in "The Crown" - one of the town's inns and rumoured to be caused by a thoughtless servant throwing out hot ashes onto a yard area too near to a pile of dry straw.

"The Angel" at Baldock provided them with lodgings for the night affording ample accommodation in the inn yard for Dobbin to be stabled and their cart to be stored.

Their talk after supper was all full of what they would do when they got home; Ann had introduced the subject of a possible move from the fen country, to some region more suited to Isaac's health consideration; it fell on deaf ears, as she well knew it would now that he was feeling back on form again and such a notion was not on his horizon; his major intention he had advised her was that he'd need to work harder at the mill to make up for all the time lost through his incapacity. Her heart had frozen at the thought of this but that was her Isaac and she, as any good wife should, must support him in his decisions; all the same – she would not lose track of the doctor's advice and keep the thought at the back of her mind and thinking that it may well be, that sometime in the future circumstances would present themselves to enable a move; a move to a part of the country with a climate and atmosphere which would not be so guaranteed to bring on his pain and suffering.

In truth, she would have liked to be nearer to her mother and her sisters; she had really missed them after moving to Lincolnshire and the brief stop-over on their way to Bath had created an idea in her mind that it might be good to be nearer to her family; she would put it to Isaac sometime – but she would have to chose her moment – but not just yet – this was not the right time – they would at least have to get back to Boston first.

Although, she did love Boston and it was special, if only because it was where her children had been born – and she had to admit that it was their home. Not the biggest of houses but not the smallest either and it was so convenient to everything – including a short walk for Isaac to the windmill on the other side of the town. The St. Anne's Terrace property had three bedrooms – well in truth one of them was little more than a box room which Elizabeth had the run of – another, which was larger and had two windows, contained the boys; a bit cramped but they all managed – without too much squabbling. Their own bedroom had an East-facing window so the sun was with them early in the morning; Ann liked that very much. Outside there was really no garden worth speaking about – just a back yard with a couple trees, a lilac bush and an assortment of plants in barrels and buckets; Isaac delighted in looking at his flowers grown from the tiny seeds and bulbs he took a great delight in collecting. When the weather would permit, they would both sit out of an evening – listening to the sounds of the river which ran at the back of them and the birds settling down for the night. Being so near to The Stump – they were treated to the nightly displays of the bats diving and swooping on silken wings likes puffs of silent smoke gobbling up the lazy twilight insects.

Isaac had been a good and prudent provider – the whole house, before they had moved in, being filled and fitted with everything she could want or need. She would have liked to be more involved with the furnishing and the purchasing but being over a hundred and twenty miles away in Kelvedon, made it difficult, to say the least. Deborah – her sister-in-law who lived locally – gave a helping hand in choosing things – though she had her hands full with eight children but she was happy to give a little of her time. Her husband, Isaac's brother Thomas, his partner in the milling business, also helped and between them all they had the place up and running when Isaac brought her back after their Kelvedon wedding. Ann had made just a few re-arrangements and added her own touch over the eleven years they had lived there; by now the house was very much to her own and to Isaac's own liking. But she would be happy to leave all that behind and move to somewhere else if it would be beneficial to Isaac's health. She had thought to herself – prayer must be brought to bear in this matter – and pray she did – that God would show them the way.

Oh dear she remarked to herself – still seated at the dressing table – the time – look at the time; I must get myself down to the dining room.

When she did arrive at the table – James was taking the soup and was looking quite perplexed. Ann – all of a fluster sat in the chair opposite him.

"Mother – I was quite concerned that something was the matter with you."

"Yes – well – you shouldn't concern yourself – I was quite alright; I just dawdled a little too long in getting myself ready."

The waiter served her soup and she took up the spoon and began her meal.

"It's probably cold by now mother."

"No James – it's just right."

"What delayed you?"

"Oh – nothing much – just going over things in my mind – that's all."

"And you are feeling alright are you?"

"Perfectly James!"

"Are you getting a little home sick mother?"

"Yes – a little – but it's nothing for you to concern yourself about."

"If you like we can give Pisa a miss – and head home tomorrow."

"Of course not James – you've been so looking forward to visiting the place – it would be silly to miss the chance of a visit, seeing that we are comparatively so near; who knows when we will return again."

"Right then – that's fine. I'm really looking forward to seeing that famous tower and climb to the top – but if you wanted to be back home – then that would be alright too."

"Thank you James – we will go to Pisa – but I'm not sure about this climbing of the tower. It may tax you considerably James." She didn't want to venture any more because she was close to tears and wasn't about to make a show of herself; but he was right – she would have loved, that very minute, to just pack everything and go home. But would she feel any better at home? Maybe it was the best thing that they had been away for a while – nothing to remind her of dearest Isaac; nothing that is except her thoughts and the pictures her mind made; was it all so very long ago?

Chapter nineteen

Anne felt that somehow, the nearer they were getting to home – the longer the journey seemed to take; it was almost as if The Great North Road was stretching itself like a worm and home was getting further away. They were making for Huntingdon – not quick such a big jump as the last journey they had made – though it was tempting to try fur further; but their good and faithful servant Dobbin must be considered coupled with the fact that Isaac had wanted to see the birthplace of Oliver Cromwell – whom Isaac felt had lost his way; considering that his original high minded principles gave way to the the desire for power and the putting to the sword those who held against him. He had, however, taken a lenient stand against the Quakers and was greatly impressed by George Fox, the founder of The Society Of Friends. Isaac told her that when Quakers were being persecuted, after a meeting Cromwell had with George Fox – he gave the order that they were to be left alone and so they were.

Before crossing the river, The Great Ouse, in Huntingdon they stopped briefly at Godmanchester – the name of the town greatly intriguing Isaac. They had both mused upon the name – Ann supposing that it may have come from a possible association with a good man who had lived there – or at least something to do with God; Isaac – as was his custom when he wanted to know something, asked at the village pump – what was the derivation of the name and came back quite disappointed to learn that it was supposed to be named after Godmund, a Roman lord, who founded a settlement there, creating a stopping off place for the Roman armies marching north. There was a very suitable inn there where they could have stayed but Isaac wanted to get that few miles further.

Their road from Godmanchester took them alongside Portholme Meadow – the biggest meadow in the country – so Isaac said and completely surrounded by water;, the only way to get on the meadow being by crossing a bridge, with yet another curious name – The Chinese Bridge – which seemingly had only been built four years previously, to replace an older bridge.

Once Isaac had seen the birthplace of Oliver Cromwell they took rooms for the night with a temperance establishment, much favoured by Quaker visitors travelling along The Great North Road; it proved to be both comfortable and cheap, appealing to them in both ways, their funds now getting a little low – but yet Isaac considered, enough to get them home.

They didn't leave Huntingdon till mid – morning – taking a look at some of the interesting buildings there including Hinchingbrooke House where Oliver Cromwell was born and where his family still lived; they went to look at a castle which stood in Huntingdon and was fortified by Cromwell but was now but ruins, so they didn't spend much time there.

Peterborough was a much bigger and more important place with a cathedral which, when they visited, was in a state of much needed restoration, having s uffered greatly during the period of The Civil War.

The original plan was for them to make for Grantham after Peterborough, with maybe a stop on the way. But Isaac considered that the road from Grantham to Boston was a better road – and one used by the stage coaches, assuring other users of a better state of repair; but when they got to Peterborough – they were both longing to be home – and so Isaac decided to set off early and push for home going through Spalding, where they had Quaker friends they could stay with if need be.

As it turned out – they did need to stop over in Spalding – poor Dobbin was too tired to make it to Boston – and the roads were not good, there having been heavy rain overnight. Just another 15 miles to go and they would be home.

They met up with a farmer who was driving some sheep over to the market in Boston – he was going to set off as they arrived at Peterborough and break the back of the journey before it became dark; he told them there was a field they could use halfway for an overnight stay and feeding for his flock – then he would set off to Boston market at first light. This would mean he'd arrive in Boston a goodly while before they would and he promised to calls at St. Anne's Terrace and let the children know that they were on the way.

Isaac suggested it would give Bessie time to get her foot behind the boys and make sure everything was clean and tidy for their return; Ann ventured that if she knew her daughter, she shouldn't be surprised if the boot hadn't been behind the boys from the day they left.

Their friends at Spalding were delighted to see them and

especially seeing that Isaac was so well – and as they said – a new man walked through their door. Ann expected that when they were back home this was going to be the general reaction of most people; but it was true – he did look well – as anybody would who is free of pain.

Back in the land of waterways – as most of that part of Lincolnshire was, with the inevitable little bridges going over them. Windmills greeted their eyes – dotted about all over the place but these were not grinding corn but having their wind power applied to draining the land which had been under water since the creation.

Ever nearer home and the sight Ann was wanting to see - "The Stump" - the steeple of St. Botolph's Church and there in the shadow of that amazing construction, would be their own little home and their much loved children. How could she have left them? But left them she had – but only to return as now with a father back to the fullest of good health, as the wonderful man seated next to her was.

It was all very familiar territory now – Kirton and St. Peter & St. Paul's church – then through Wyberton and the church of St. Leodegar – only two more miles to go; as they turned the bend coming out of Wyberton there in the distance was "The Stump".

"Soon be home now Ann."

"Yes we will," and her heart was beating so that she thought it might burst.

"It's a lovely word Isaac - home. A small word and yet it means so much to us."

"That little word home – means so much to everyone Ann."

"But our home is different – our home is very special; it's not the house or the things in it – but you and I and our children."

"Are you ready for them jumping all over you Ann."

Yes she was – and the joy of walking through the door with her beloved Isaac.

It was after dinner at their Genoa hotel, that these thoughts were passing through her mind; no Isaac would walk through any door by her side now but she knew, that in many ways, he was still with her.

It was all she could do not to turn and say - "Do you remember that Isaac?"

She just caught the tail end of something that James was saying to his new friends – it was his mention of Boston.

"Isn't that so mother."

She was somewhat nonplussed – and must have looked so. James chuckled.

"Do forgive me" she said to the people in their company, "what was it about Boston, James?"

"Mr. Hunt was saying that some many years ago he had visited Boston and I was saying that was were you used to live."

She thought, how strange that Boston should come into the conversation just then – but then again – should she be surprised at anything at these times; her mind seemed to be dwelling on two levels and at two different times. Her recollections were so real she could have reached out and touched them but she was equally certain that there would have been an abundance of things that would have passed her memory by.

"Amazing church – and a famous steeple!" - this was Mr. Hunt, "said to be the biggest in the land."

Ann – smiled – The Stump was often mentioned when people discovered that she had lived in Boston; she wondered if everyone in the World new about Boston and its famous 'Stump'.

"Not a doubt of it Mr. Hunt" Ann replied gaily, "our humble abode in St. Anne's terrace was in the shadow of the great building. It attracted many visitors – especially on market days – which were a big enough attraction in themselves."

That was where it all began; but it was a new beginning. Had she not met Abigail that day – she would not have known about Bath and the great cures being effected there – her beloved being one of them. She wanted to tell them all about it but somehow it didn't seem the right thing to say and yet it seemed highly appropriate.

"Was 'The Stump' your church Mrs. Reckitt?"

"Well – we certainly lived in the parish – and yes my husband and I would go to a service from time to time – usually when there was an advertised notable minister addressing the congregation; but our regular Sunday devotionals took place at The Friends Meeting House – a far less, shall we say, impressive building."

There then followed a conversation about Quakers and people known to the Hunts who adopted the Quaker way of life. For Ann – this went on for far too long and she yearned for the solitude of her room. The Hunts were very friendly and interesting people – and she did appreciate their company; they had quite taken to James – for which she was grateful but she would be glad to alone with her own thoughts just now. James was happy to remain chatting to to them and so she excused herself and retired to her room.

She sat awhile by the window – which did not have the best of views being situated at the rear of the hotel but they were not to remain at the hotel for very long; but it did have a very comfortable chair and so it sufficed her very well. Soon her thoughts drifted back to their coming home to Boston.

Undoubtedly her excitement at seeing her children again was foremost in her mind, as they drove along High Street but at the same time a sense of foreboding tempered her high spirits.

Soon they were over town bridge, coming into the market place; all around was just had they had left it; The Stump towered over all the other buildings, which were none the less impressive – Fydell House – now looking the worse for damage caused by a riot in the town, some of the windows being smashed in.

They were indeed troubled times for fen country people; everyone was suffering from the dreadful corn laws; in many ways Ann would be glad to be out of the place. Maybe Isaac would see that too – but she could never tell with Isaac; he certainly presented himself as a man of courage but his courage was not the kind that takes a man to war. For that she was profoundly grateful. She upheld the belief that wars would never solve anything except the putting of money into the hands of gun and powder merchants; or increasing the profits of the armoury makers and sadly line the pockets of undertakers.

Home at last; she would preserve that vision forever – walking through her own front door again – looking around her kitchen to see if anything had changed. One things was for certain – it was clean; she knew it would have been with her darling Bessie in charge.

She could still sense the smell of something good in the oven; there were tears in both their eyes when the children came bounding in from their bedrooms – Bessie's voice could be heard on the landing - "No running!"

It didn't make a ha'porth of difference – into the kitchen they came like some army nearly knocking her and Isaac over with their welcome.

"Steady on there – steady one we've only been gone for five minutes!"

"But father – you've been away for years – we didn't think you were coming back." This was from Charles – the eldest and the gentlest; the others just clamoured around; Bessie wanted to know everything we had done and seen. It was a truly joyous homecoming but we were both glad when it was bedtime. Our own bed; but tired as we were, sleep, would not claim us.

"It does seem like we've been away for a long time – doesn't it my love?"

"Indeed it does Ann – we shouldn't have left them you know; me and my ailments – we are both a nuisance." "That's quite enough of that talk Isaac Reckitt; you are well now – you have been cured – we are back home with our children – our prayers have been answered and that's all that matters." "But how long will it last?"

She pressed his head to her shoulder and stroked his cheek; Isaac – bold – confident – sometimes immoderate in debate and forceful in his opinions – was at heart a little boy himself.

"Isaac – do you not think we should take the doctor's advice?"

This came out as a natural progression from the words Isaac had spoken; it wasn't pre-planned – it hadn't been her intention to take up the subject quite so soon after their homecoming. There was no immediate response – not unknown for Isaac; though his general habit was to be quick off the mark in his responses – almost answering the question before it had been asked. Several minutes passed by before there was an answer; in fact it seemed so long in coming that she thought he'd maybe gone to sleep – but when the answer came it was quite gentle in tone.

"Yes, my dear loving wife – we should take the doctor's advice but you'll have to give me time to put things in order; my absence won't have helped the business so I must put it on a steady footing; I owe that much to Thomas. He will have carried a heavy load whilst we have been away. It is my duty to do what I can."

That was Isaac – honour and duty where everything to him.

"You are a good man Isaac Reckitt – and I love you for it."

It wasn't long before Isaac had drifted off to the land of slumber and dreams; sweet ones she hoped. But sleep would not come for her; she still was possessed with a feeling of uneasiness – wondering what tomorrow would bring; what the outcome of his returning to the mill should be. Oh yes –

176

Thomas would be delighted to have him back in the business again but was there a possibility that he might have doubts about the future of the partnership; would he perhaps have got used to organising everything and effecting the undertakings of the business his own way. She had to admit to the possibility, that though a loving brother he certainly was, he might feel a little resentment about Isaac's return; such were the thoughts that claimed her mind till she said aloud to herself

"Tomorrow will bring what it will bring but today must bring sleep."

And with that she too joined Isaac in the land of slumber and rest; though not as restful as it could have been but inevitably the new day would dawn and take care of itself.

Chapter twenty

"You always give me too much food in my pack-up."

"Well – dear husband of mine – I don't want you to go hungry – but what you can't eat – you can share; or you can share anyway."

There was something special about getting his snap box together again; not a task she'd performed for some time – even before they went away – Isaac didn't go the the mill for weeks, so there was no need to make up a carry-out box for him.

As she waved him off – it was just like the old times; she watched him walking down the terrace – passing the church to his left – then into the marketplace before disappearing into Narrow Bar Gate; at the corner, he turned and waved to her and she waved back.

As she stood for a few moments at the door, her eyes had filled with tears and she hoped that no one had been looking but as she turned to close the door – there behind her was her daughter Bessie; they looked at each other for a moment – then Bessie ran to her mother; Ann held her close and they both cried. Nothing was said – but then there was no need to with her and her daughter; both needed the comfort that each extended to the other – woman to woman.

"Come on now – dry those tears; we have work to do."

"Not too much work I hope; did I not do a good job of looking after the house."

"You did a wonderful job looking after the house – but there's still unpacking to do and washing to be done and …….."

She very nearly said "And Dobbin to see to" - but there was no Dobbin to see to – they had returned him to his owners last night – along with the low-loading cart. Isaac had wanted to give their friends some money for the use of their equine champion and the cart he pulled but this had been politely refused with the words, "But what can you owe us after coming back to us so well – that surely is reward enough; and another thing – Dobbin will have something to tell the others in the stable; something to boast about; why – none of them have ever been to London or any of the other places you've visited."

All the places they had visited! Yes – thought Ann – it would be something for her to tell everyone about but she would have traded the whole experience for a husband in good health.

She meant what she said when she'd told Bessie she had done a good job looking after the house – everything was perfect; and being with her children once more was the most perfect thing of all. In the comparatively short time that they had been away, they all seemed to have grown so much; it was almost as if they were not children any more – but of course they were but not looking after them on a daily basis for such a long time it now seemed like something strange.

The things that go through a body's head thought Ann to herself; what seemed to her quite amazing, was that she felt she could almost reach out and touch that feeling of so many years ago; sitting down at the kitchen table and sharing a pot of tea with her daughter and a chat before the boys came to life from their slumbers.

"Mother – you won't have to go away again will you?"

"I certainly hope not Bessie."

"We all missed you and father much."

"No more than we missed you – I can assure you of that."

"Promise you won't go away again."

Children; things seem so very black and white to them – but what they don't realise is that life isn't like that; she would have been happy to make the promise that her daughter had asked her to make – but should she do that? It would have been easy to say the words that Bessie had wanted to hear but who knew what the future would hold.

"Bessie – if it was only up to me – I would most surely make that promise but the future is in hands far greater than mine, hands that will always provide the very best for us. We may not appreciate it at the time – but we must all believe it to be so."

It wasn't the answer her daughter wanted but she managed a watery smile and their hands reached out across the table and were clasped in mutual understanding.

Once they had all breakfasted and the children got themselves off to school Ann spent an hour or so just going from room to room; opening cupboards and drawers – reaching up to shelves and handling the things on them. She wasn't quite sure why she was doing this but it gave her a great deal of pleasure and in a way the re-assurance that this

180

was their home.

Maybe these actions were prompted by the sense of uneasiness which still possessed her; it would go – once she had resumed her routine – broken by their going away. What would she do first? Well – getting the fire lit under the copper would be a good idea; there was quite a substantial amount of washing to be attended to; then she must bake – a task that always soothed her – the kneading of the dough; the beating of the eggs for the cakes and the sense of satisfaction she felt when what she put into the oven came out well.

So that was the plan for the day – and the copper was certainly filled with water and the fire underneath it lit; no sooner had this task been completed when there was a knock at the door – succeeded by a succession of other knocks as one by one their friends arrived to welcome them home; each bringing a little something for the table. Soon the table began to look like a market stall; cakes and pastries – bottles of fruit – early summer vegetables and an assortment of meats and brawns.

Her last visitor was Abigail; dear Abigail – the friend she would remember for the rest of her life. If it hadn't been for that chance meeting at the market – what would things have been like now? She shuddered to think – it was almost too fearful to contemplate the consequences; Isaac's illness would certainly not have not got better; oh – the warmer weather may well have brought with it some relief from the pain he suffered but it would have been only temporary.

During that first full day back – almost everything that took place brought with it some joy; the very simplest of tasks was to Ann another bonus. She decided make their evening meal a celebration and prepared all the things that she knew Isaac and the children enjoyed most; her pleasure and satisfaction would come from their pleasure and enjoyment.

Isaac had said that he wouldn't be late home so that they could all eat together; sometimes it would be dark before he came in for his meal and often the children had eaten and were ready for bed before their father returned but today they were all going to eat together.

It was the boys who were first through the door — disputing as usual who was first to the door; Elizabeth followed a little after with Charles — they were not for the race and happy to walk leisurely — Elizabeth could have raced but chose to walk at a steadier pace with her older brother.

"What's for tea mum?"

"Well George — I thought you might enjoy a broth I've made with your old boots."

They were much taken with this jest and much laughter ensued.

Young as Francis was he could be quite droll and had his own contribution - "But mother — what are we going to play out in if we eat our old boots."

At this the others were convulsed with laughter.

"You'll have play out in what the good Lord provided you with — your two feet."Elizabeth and George came through the door with her daughter saying, "We could smell your baking all the way down the street."

"And it was a most delightful aroma." From George.

"I'm very glad to hear it — because I've worked myself dizzy preparing all the things you all like best."

"When can we start mum? I'm starving." - this was from Frederick – who always seemed to be hungry.

"We will all sit down at the table together when your father comes home; he'll be back with us soon."

"We've just seen father walking across the market place with uncle Thomas."

"Oh – did he say anything to you?"

"I don't think he saw us – he was in deep conversation with uncle Thomas."

"I wonder where they were going."

"They were going past the guild hall when we came along on the other side of the street."

I wonder why your father and uncle Thomas were going past the guild hall; the only place they might visit down that way is the offices of Mr Jebb their solicitor."

"Well he'll arrive when he arrives mother – and not a minute sooner; so don't worry yourself; I'm sure we won't die of starvation if we wait a little longer."

This brought groans from the younger ones – but Elizabeth added - "Any way – how can we possibly sit down to eat with you grubby boys; you look like you've been down the mine digging coal. Out to the pump with you!" And she scooted them off into the back yard.

That sense of uneasiness she'd been feeling since they came back from Bath – now returned; in truth it hadn't gone away – but as normality seemed to be returning, it had become less.

Charles her eldest – ever the sensitive one put his hand on

her shoulder. "There's something troubling you mother – isn't there?"

"I wouldn't say exactly troubling me but I have to admit to a slight feeling of uneasiness; it's probably nothing – just the homecoming and seeing you all again; it will be fine."

But she knew that she wouldn't be at ease until I saac came home; why would he want to go to the solicitor's office with Thomas?

The time was going on – an hour had passed and she couldn't keep the children from their meal any longer and so she served some food up for them, saying that she could wait for her meal until their father came home. Prayers were said and they tucked into the special treats Ann had cooked up for them.

An atmosphere prevailed in the kitchen – Ann wasn't chatty as she usually was – asking her little brood what they had done at school today; the children seemed to pick up on her anxiety. Ann looked at the clock – they looked at the clock; Ann's glanced towards the window – they glanced towards the window.

It wasn't like Isaac at all; he was a man known for his punctuality and at other times, if he had known he was going to be late for their evening meal, he would have sent one of the boys from the mill to tell her. Things could happen in the mills; it was not unknown for a miller to be killed in the course of his daily work; just one slip and he might find himself trapped in the mechanism – or hit by the sails – or any one of a dozen things. But at least he had been seen walking down the street with his brother – so that possibility was not worrying

184

her.

All was very quiet in the kitchen now – just the sound of knives and forks on plates and the occasional shuffle of a chair. Ann had now seated herself at the table by the window and was mending some of their stockings; there were quite a number of mends requiring her attention – but she was happy to undertake the task, moreover it was, in a way, an indication that she had been missed.

Everything had settled into its own level of quietness so that when the sound of the latch came, the noise was out of proportion; in reality it was more like the crashing sound of a pan falling off the table.

"The children were getting hungry so I gave them their meal." Isaac just looked at her for a few long moments and then responding in an abstracted way.

"What – oh yes – our meal; sorry if I've kept you from your food."

"I've got our meal in the oven – would you like to eat now?"

For a moment he seemed at a loss for an answer – then he produced what was very clearly a forced smile and an air of jocularity.

"In the oven? But it should be in us – let us make no delay or we will waste away to nothing."

Laughter ensued from the children and the atmosphere was broken, yet Ann knew in her heart that something was not right. Isaac disappeared into the scullery and she heard the sound of him drawing water with which to wash himself. He would have normally changed from his working clothes before he sat down at the table but on this occasion he forewent this particular routine.

"And what has the school, for which we pay a King's ransom for, taught you all today."

"A king's ransom father – does it cost as much as that for our learning." This was from Bessie.

"It costs double for a girl – it's a wonder we have enough left to put food on the table."

Giggles ensued and as he gazed upon Ann he gave her a wink and she clicked her tongue in mock disapproval; the little knot that was forming in her stomach slackened somewhat and she got on with serving their meal up on the table.

"We've eaten all ours up like good children – can we go out to play?"

Ann gave Isaac a glance for his agreement to the request but he looked distant again as if he hadn't heard the request.

"Is that alright Isaac?"

"Sorry – what was that?"

"George was asking if they could go out to play."
Isaac looked at them with mock severity – and a twinkle in his eye.

"Out to play – but that's only what children do."

"But we are children father," piped up Frederick.

"Well – I never – there was me thinking that you were members of the town council preparing some great piece of legislation."

This produced loud guffaws from the older ones – but the word puzzled Francis – her youngest.

"We can't do legislation father – we – don't even know what it is."

She thought Bessie was going to fall off her chair, her laughter convulsing her and the more she laughed the more did everyone else; Isaac could keep this sort of banter going for ages – and no one enjoyed it more than Bessie.

"Go on then – be off with you; keep an eye on them Bessie and make sure they don't have too much fun!"

Just the two of them remained in the kitchen; Ann placed the food on the table and Isaac drew up a chair – now bowing his head to give thanks for their food; he would always carry out this ritual standing behind his chair; Ann waited for him to be seated before she took her place beside him.

"And never let us forgot, dear Lord, that you go before us in all our doings and guide us in the way of doing thy will in all things."

This was a bit extra to his normal thanksgiving for the food on the table but he must have some reason – she didn't ask and along with her husband got on with the meal.

"How went the day Isaac?"

He didn't answer her straight away but put down his knife and fork; no words came he seemed to be taking time to formulate what he was going to say; then he resumed his eating.

"We'll talk about it later."

And she knew that would be when they had said their prayers and were lying side by side in their bed and right at that moment this seemed that it was a million hours away and would permit for too much thinking to take place; but she couldn't help these things going over in her mind.

She must have revealed something in the expression she

was wearing as she looked at him.

"Later Ann."

Chapter twenty-one

After the children were all tucked up in bed – Ann came down to the kitchen and taking up her sewing, seated herself on the settle by the fire; it wasn't cold – in fact the day had been quite warm but nights could get chilly. Their house being in the shadow of The Stump meant that, often in the daylight hours, they didn't get a great deal of sun to warm the building up; in fact the rear of the house was often the warmest – and though they didn't have a lot in the way of a garden – what Isaac did plant out, always seemed to flourish. Isaac, as was his wont, was seated at the table making entries in the accounts book; as she had sat down he'd looked up briefly from his preoccupation – and smiled at her – but said nothing.

She would have to leave it at that; he would speak when he was ready – she knew it was futile to press him into conversation when he was working on the books. Eventually the task completed he closed up the ledger and placed it carefully upon the kitchen dresser; gave it a pat – and came once more to his seat at the table.

"Will you take your hot milk now Isaac?"

"Yes my love, we shall have our hot milk now and I shall satisfy your curiosity."

She ventured a wry grin at him. "Curiosity Isaac?" He returned her wry grin with one of his own.

"Oh – come now Ann, ever since I walked in you've been wondering what it was all about."

"Well – I can't deny that would be totally correct, my dearest husband but you must confess that you have created something of a mystery with your actions."

"Nothing mysterious at all Ann; Thomas and I needed to see Mr Jebb – our worthy solicitor – to .... well – to go over a few things."

At this point he lit his pipe; he didn't smoke the pipe a great deal – in fact it was only of an evening that from the rack on the mantle shelf, he took down the old smoking piece; it was a 21st birthday present from his uncle, along with the stone jar which contained the smoking mixture. An over indulgence in tobacco was not something that Isaac approved of and he was known to speak quite severely about men who wasted money on tobacco when their families needed food in their bellies. And though not a total abstainer, he also held the same views about alcoholic beverages.

Ann poured out the hot milk into their mugs and grated a small amount of nutmeg into each of them along with a generous spoonful of honey. This accomplished, she once more seated herself by the fire and took up her sewing; she could wait. She would have to wait; when Isaac was good and ready – he would give forth.

Half the beverage had been consumed and great clouds of smoke had been launched into the kitchen air when Isaac cleared his throat and began to speak.

"Things are not good with the mill my dear."

"But you knew that before we went away."

"Yes – I did know that – but in the short time we have been away – the decline has deepened to the point that some drastic action is needed. We are beset with high corn prices which make our products too costly for the ordinary people to buy and the rich know that they have us over a barrel and demand ever lower prices till we are practically down to the bone."

"What can be done Isaac?"

"Well for one thing – we can tell them to take their business elsewhere."

"And will they do that?"

"OH yes Ann – they will do that. So the cost of running the mill must be addressed. In short it won't support the wages; we have to cut down – and that includes both Thomas and myself."

"I'd no idea things were so bad."

He finished off the rest of his hot milk and took his mug to the slop-stone and rinsed it out. Ann continued to drink hers as he came and sat beside her on the settle – he put his arm around her shoulder and held her close to him.

"OH Ann – I seem to court disaster – don't I."

What could she say; he had experienced more than his fair share of misfortune – more than most people but then he had more ambition than most; had more vision – along with the consequences that all too often plague all visionaries – disappointment.

"Ann – I've never witnessed such distress – as that present in Thomas when he updated me with the situation."

"So what will happen now?"

"What indeed?"

Despite all the potential gloom that this revelation might well have brought with it – there was also a positive side – a side that carried her along on the wave of hope; their hand had been forced – the door was open to a move. It would cost – she was sure of that but they had a good family who she knew would not turn away when help was needed. God works in mysterious ways his wonders to perform and somewhere in all of this there was most surely the hand of God.

From her room in their Genoa hotel, she could see the ornate towers and steeples of at least five churches; the houses of God they called them. Certainly, they possessed all the trappings of a God centred belief – but was God there within all that elaborate masonry and statuary, any more than he was here with her now in this very room? It was the way people liked their places of worship to be but not all people of course – some preferred things to be quite different; Quaker Friends would always much prefer their places of worship to be of a more simple construction – without anything in the way of holy statuary and ornate furnishings; just a room where people may gather together and only big enough to accommodate the flock; a room where they could focus on the important things and not images. But the fact remained that in times of strife and tribulation people felt a sense of comfort in gathering together with other believers and it didn't really matter where or what the place looked like, for them it was common ground. Their need of God was never greater than when their backs were to the wall and there was often no other place they could turn to for help or consolation.

That night, back in Boston, she felt she needed reassurance as she had never before; reassurance that their lives where being led by God's hand – his plan for them was being played out. At the distance in time she was now from that moment she could see that everything had worked together for good.

Their evening prayers that night were very much centred along these lines; asking God to show them the way – lead them into his plan for them. In a strange sort of way – but then again not so strange really, from that moment she felt better; the forebodings which had troubled her since their return were now confronted and had been dealt with. It was the future that now mattered and upon that they both agreed, as they gave each other their goodnight kiss and settled down to take their rest.

For the next few weeks, there was so much to do it seemed like her feet had hardly touched the ground. It had been agreed that Thomas should keep the mill on and pay Isaac his share of the original capital to put into their next venture. There was nothing else that could be added to this by way of interest because there was nothing else there. Just barely surviving was how Isaac had described the business and stringent pruning was going to be needed to weather the crisis being faced. Thomas felt he was equal to the challenge of running the business on his own; that is to say on his own with his family – twelve of them; there had been fourteen children but the twins Maria and Hannah had never reached the age of twelve months, Maria being lost to them within two months of her birth and Hannah surviving for eight months longer before she had died. Four of the remaining children were boys but all of them had assured their father that they would do their share of the work; even little Caroline who was just seven at the time.

Ann thought how hard it must be for Thomas being of the mind as they all were in their abhorrence at the practice of enforced child labour. Children as young as five were being exploited by countless unscrupulous establishments and it was not unknown for little ones to be putting in a ten or twelve hour day.

Charles Dickens, through his stories, had exposed many of the horrors that were present in society; attitudes towards children, which for some, were considerably less than their attitudes towards animals; he himself at 11 years of age had been sent to work in a blacking factory where he tied labels on to bottles of boot – blacking.

It would be nothing like this with Thomas but the fact that his family could come to his aid at this particular time was a very sound reason for him taking over the running of the mill.

But the question remained, what would they do? Where would they go? In her heart she'd have liked to be closer to her mother and sisters but that must not be the main consideration. Uppermost must be the ability of Isaac to find some suitable work – work which would provide them with a living to keep her own little brood clothed and fed; although at present only four of them, their number could well be increased in the not too distant future.

As was usual with Quaker Friends, there would be gatherings to discuss their future; this was something that their local group would take a keen interest in and be eager to find a way for them to keep body and soul together.

Though the community would be sad to lose Isaac it was generally thought, that it was in his, and consequently, his family's, best interests for them all to move home to a region more compatible to his health and well-being. Most of the group had voiced the desire for them to relocate within travelling distance of Boston in order to maintain friendships, of which there were many. But if that was not to be – then they would understand.

As with all Quaker communities, someone knew someone, who knew someone else in such and such a place; people who had done well for themselves and their families – serving the towns and villages they had gone to live in and were prospering in their various occupations. Everyone wanted to do their best for the family

Isaac continued with his work at the mill – mainly to help get Thomas' sons established in all the aspects of a miller's work; showing them the way that the mill should run – giving them the benefits of his own knowledge and experience. But the longer he remained in Boston – the more likely it would be that his old condition would return.

Eventually after a great deal of discussion and talking well into the night on numerous nights, it was agreed that their move should be to Nottingham; a growing town with plenty of opportunity for enterprise and expansion.

On the face of it this was going to be a good move; a new place with new possibilities challenges – everything looked good. Money was very tight and more loans had to be secured to help them establish themselves. Isaac's share of the mill looked unlikely to materialise and in the end he told Thomas that he needn't worry about paying him back. That was her Isaac – her dear Isaac – generous to a fault but she wouldn't have had him any other way. In the event, his generosity, though much applauded by the friends meeting, had not helped a great deal – perhaps only really staved off the inevitable for Thomas; even with the knowledge that he hadn't to pay back Isaac's share and the help of his family, the business went into a steep decline, not helped by a succession of poor harvests coupled with heavy losses sustained by high prices of the cereal crops on which they were dependant; it was inevitable that two years after they had moved to Nottingham, poor Thomas was going to be declared insolvent.

This had distressed Isaac greatly and he had wanted to help but his own finances were in no great shape. There was nothing anyone could do – the mill had to be sold off and all the equipment disposed of. After all their hard work and investments – to see their venture come to this troubled Isaac for quite some time. His distress increased when he learned that Thomas had been under the scrutiny of The Quaker Movement – which was very much opposed to bankruptcy, considering it to be the equivalent of theft from those to whom the bankrupt was left owing money. Despite a good family background in the Quaker faith, their own grandfather being a well-respected Quaker missionary, Thomas was outed from their number. He appealed the decision to three different Quaker Meetings but to no avail. So eventually, through circumstances which could not be remedied, he and his family were also to find themselves moving from the area. But Thomas, to give him his due, was not down for long and having a good education himself, set up as a schoolmaster in Manchester and did very well for himself and his family.

Dear Thomas and Debora – they were both good people. She'd heard only two days ago, in a letter from home, that Thomas had taken Isaac's death badly. He was living in Chorley and not a well man himself, now in his seventy seventh year – there was concern that the effect of his brother's death might worsen his condition. Sadly he had lost his wife Debora ten years earlier.

As brothers they had been very close; it had long been Isaac's hope that they would eventually engage in some new joint undertaking together but that wasn't to be; Isaac had been sad to leave his brother behind when they departed for Nottingham.

Any move – no matter how near or how far produces its own emotions but one aspect which Ann was more concerned about was the uprooting of the children. She recalled her own family uprooting from Cley Next The Sea – and their establishing themselves in Kelvedon but that was a move forced upon them by the death of their father; and yet – it had been a good move for the family and soon they had all found their new life rich and blessed. Her mother, still a comparatively young woman, had married again and brought to birth a new addition to their family, a boy, to her existing brood of mostly girls – there being six daughters – prior to the new marriage and Kincey, then her only son; brother Kincey was delighted to have a new boy in the family.

There were so many hurdles to jump and obstacles to overcome but at least Isaac had his health back and was equal to them. Once more, her family came to their aid in helping with the finance of setting up in a new milling business and the trade of a corn merchant, for which Isaac was qualified. This hadn't proved of any major success in the past but Nottingham was a major town and a wider Quaker community with more friends to be made.

Friends they didn't know as yet had found for them a house in Popham Street which was between Canal Street and Narrow Marsh. Not too big a house but one big enough for their existing numbers with thoughts to the future. Within half an hour's walking distance was the mill which Isaac would work, situated on The River Leen.

There was no time to be wasted – the move must be made as soon as possible; what a mixture of emotions were ebbing and flowing within them all. Yes there was sadness at leaving Boston – their first home but there was also the excitement of the new venture; and with the new move she knew there was going to be a new addition to the family; they had better get a move on.

Chapter twenty-two.

And so it was that on 14th day of the 11th month of 1833, at their house in Nottingham's Popham Street, that James, her much loved youngest son, came into this world. A very mild winter as she recalled – in fact one of the mildest she ever remembered. Strange to think that the climate being so temperate for the time of the year of his birth would have been to his advantage health wise.

It was a lovely house they had in Popham Street though hardly any outside garden but enough space within for their growing family. Bessie adored her new brother and wanted to be fussing about him all the time; if she'd had her way she would have done everything for him; but that was Bessie – the little mother – but not so little now at the age of twelve and half.

Popham Street wasn't a very wide street. Ann often thought they could have almost leaned out of one of the front bedroom windows to shake hands with the people across the street; true - you would have had to have quite long arms and lean out of the window precariously. But certainly, there wasn't a lot of space between the houses - just enough to get a cart down the street.

The neighbours were good and friendly but Ann didn't make any particular friend. However, although things were going along fairly well, there was something within her that seemed to be saying that the little house in Popham Street, would not be their final home. Or indeed the town of Nottingham. Most of the time she pushed these ideas to one side and just got on with their lives as best they could.

Health wise they all seemed to be much better for the move to Nottingham; yes - it was an industrial area and chimneys abounded but the atmosphere was so much drier than in Boston. Isaac was doing really well and she was glad that she had made the difficult/arduous journey - taking him to Bath. Sometimes she looked back on that time and it all seemed like a dream and a somewhat fantastic one at that. People then had thought she was mad to undertake the journey and looking back she was inclined to think that there had been a touch of madness about it.

Her eldest son Charles - now coming up to fifteen was still a worry to her; his health was up and down - some days he was as bright as bright could be and the hopeful feeling in her was high - thinking he was going to be well. Then there were other days when he was almost confined to the house. Doctors would tell her that it was just his age and a phase he was going through and he would grow out of it.

Isaac was of the opinion that he should have been sent to Ackworth School - but she had always been favoured against Charles being sent away. Ann insisted that there was nothing wrong with Packham's Academy, attended by all of them.

George Packham, the principal of the Academy, which was in Nottingham's Castle Gate was a very well respected man and countless numbers of children had been set upon the right road in life through his tutelage. It was a very progressive, noted, educational establishment where the pupils were given a very sound education in all manner of subjects, even boasting a laboratory; another bonus for Ann's children attending the school was that it was only five minutes' walk from Popham Street. And further more the walk avoided some of the less savoury areas of the city where drunkenness appeared to be the norm.

Ann did not have the highest opinion of Ackworth School - true it was a well-respected boarding school amongst the Quaker Society Of Friends and had amongst its pupils some who achieved great fame in the World but in her opinion some of the living side of life there was sparse to say the least; when Ann attended she had run away and so her mother took her out and continued her education herself.

Life in Nottingham was anything but easy for Isaac; though the climate was much better than the climate of the fen country but despite much hard work his endeavours were not to flourish as much as they had both hoped. The much-detested Corn Laws were still in existence and would be for many more years to come, affecting trades people and the population in general by forcing prices for imported grain artificially high. Many had stood against the corn laws but always they had been defeated in their protest.

Isaac traded in Nottingham as a miller and corn merchant — that was what he was apprenticed to, with his uncle Isaac in Norfolk and though he was not afraid to get onto his feet at public meetings and give his opinion about matters of the day including the Corn Laws, it was from his milling and corn merchanting that he earned his daily bread.

Who knows – perhaps if Isaac had adopted one of the other trades flourishing at that time, they might have remained in Nottingham – which Ann felt was without doubt a beautiful town.

Lace making and hosiery were high amongst the most successful industries in Nottingham but neither, she feared, would have been to Isaac's taste. He would consider them as fripperies - particularly the fancier end of hosiery; some of the lace too was considered by Quakers as too much; the simple style of attire needed no such additions.

One of Nottingham's major problems was that although the population was growing, the sanitation facilities were not keeping up with the times. In the very same year that James was born, Nottingham saw a most dreadful cholera epidemic which took the lives of over three hundred people.

Ann was very much fearful for the health of her family but though illness was no stranger to the Reckitt household, the dreadful cholera disease did not touch them. They would be counted amongst the survivors of the epidemic and for that Ann would always give thanks.

Eight mouths to provide food for was no easy task for Isaac but he was determined to keep going. Fortunately, his health held out and he was able to apply the energy needed to keep the family heads above water. But for most of the time it was just an existence.

It seemed like no time at all since James had been born and he was only just about walking, when Ann discovered that there was another child on the way. This was not something she would have planned but the good Lord in his wisdom granted people children in his time plan and they gave thanks. Almost two years to the day of James' birth, their second daughter, Constance, came into this world.

Elizabeth was delighted to have a sister at last; five brothers were enough for any girl - though James was exceedingly special to her, always being known as "Little Brother" - even until he was a great deal older.

James too adored his new little sister and was happy to play with her and give her his full attention – and Constance in return loved him. Being the two youngest they were very close to each other and it was a great sadness to James when his darling Constance was taken from this life at just eleven years of age. But that was still yet to come.

Chapter twenty-three.

"Well mother – are we ready?"

"Yes James – we are ready."

Bags packed – it was time to make their departure from Genoa. Ann had enjoyed the stay there but was happy to move on – what's more she was delighted at the amazing change in her son. His breathing was almost normal and the coughing had nearly ceased altogether, except when he exerted himself too much. He was a different boy and she gave thanks for it as each day passed. How bountiful was the Lord in all his goodness?

As they travelled the road out of Genoa which climbed many hundreds of feet above the sea, she marvelled at the richness of the vegetation – olives, and figs abounding and yet only the fourth month of the year. But it was so hot – it must have been 90 degrees on the Fahrenheit scale and not a great deal cooler in the shade.

And as they travelled the road to Specia – their next destination, Ann's thoughts took her back to a very different temperature and a rainy day in Nottingham in the same month of the year of 1840; with the rain came another fall – being in the fortunes of the milling business. My poor Isaac thought Ann – he deserved better for he was a truly hard worker but there came a point that year when his hard work and diligence was to prove inadequate. Letters went to and fro to members of the family from all parts of the country including Isaac's brother John and his sister Sarah who had married Nainby Kitching – and both residing in Kingston-Upon-Hull. Other friends from Isaac's Wainfleet days had also moved to Kingston-Upon-Hull and were doing well and so it was decided to cut their losses and move to Kingston-Upon-Hull where another mill was available.

So, it was in July 1840 that the family took up lodgings at 21 Bourne Street. Isaac had assured Ann that this was only to be a temporary measure until they could find somewhere better to move to live – a house of their own for their family.

So, for the third time Isaac embarked upon an enterprise as a miller, with some corn merchanting added. Ann supported Isaac in everything he did - she was firmly by his side on whatever road he took. But despite both their efforts, it seemed no time at all that this latest milling venture was going to go the way of the other two, and it was soon to become self-evident that this milling endeavour had proved to be yet another business failure. Isaac's dealings now came under the scrutiny of Kingston-Upon-Hull meeting of The Society Of Friends – the Quaker community. They were very concerned that Isaac had three business failures to his name, and despite circumstances being such that the reasons for the collapse were out of his control, questions were asked as to the possibility of Isaac being outed from the society.

This distressed Isaac and Ann greatly for both were dedicated members of the society. In the event Isaac was not outed but the fact that he may have been caused Ann to write in her diary her profound misgivings as to the way certain members of the society set themselves up as judge and jury. Ann felt that some of the unavoidable circumstances in the conduct of business were often leading to decisions which drove members from The Society and that was wrong.

Ann must have made an expostulation at this point for it caused James to turn to her with a start.

"Is everything alright mother?"

"Yes James - everything's just fine."

"You've been so quiet since we left Genoa and suddenly you blurt out *wrong.*"

"Did I really." She chuckled, "I must have been giving vent to my thoughts."

"Would you like to share them?"

"Oh - you know James - my mind has been a-wandering at times."

"Wandering mother?"

"Yes - wandering; walking down the paths of life which your father and I trod on life's journey and thinking about some of the injustices that plagued our early years together."

"I know some of it mother and I know what you went through to support father and all of us - and I've said it before and I'll no doubt say it again - you were a wife in ten thousand."

"James - I wish you wouldn't say that. I only did what any other decent and loving wife and mother would have done."

"But mother - the way you drove the horse and cart all the way to Bath with father lying paralysed in the back of it and you just a young woman of thirty-three, was nothing short of heroic."

Ann smiled at her lovely son and stroked his cheek.

"You feel so much - don't you James; you are a very tender hearted young man."

He smiled back at her and she knew he understood her need to wander down the paths of life; in way - it was part of her grieving. Oh yes she knew that very well - indeed she was grieving but somehow looking back over their lives together acted as a balm to the hurt and sorrow that was in her heart.

The drive to Specia was long, dusty and for the most part exhausting; Ann could hardly wait to get to their destination and wash away the heat and dust of the day. Rooms had been booked ahead for them at The Broce de Malta which Ann considered a comfortable and well served inn.

They had lunch on the way and dinner was to be the next meal - served at 6pm so there was plenty of time for Ann to wash, change her attire and have an hour of quietness.

Once that hour was achieved she was back in Nottingham recalling those days which were very happy days. She would take the children down to the River Leen where their father worked the corn mill. It was wonderfully territory for Frederick, George and Francis who played endless games and loved to swim in the river. Charles wouldn't be joining in with any of this but was happy to watch his siblings having fun.

They would often walk down to King's Meadow and picnic there; this is of course when the river wasn't flooding which it did when there had been bouts of heavy rain.

Looking back she had been really sad to leave Nottingham and Popham St. It was small but a happy house. But now it was rooms in Bourne Street - though Isaac had said it wouldn't be for long. She knew he would do his best to find somewhere more permanent for them to live. Bourne Street was, however, very near to the town centre.

Once again the family rallied round us; loans came in from several relatives including my mother. In Isaac she must have seen a man just waiting for the right opportunity to come along - and along it came in the form of something Isaac had no previous experience of - starch-making. It was a competitive market and a number of manufacturers had got a foothold in sales of the product but Isaac believed there could be room for one more. At first it was just collars and cuffs to which starch was applied but then the practice spread to all linen including bed sheets and pillows.

Through the family and local Kingston-Upon-Hull connections, knowledge came that it appeared that there was a small starch works available in the north bank area of the river Hull. It had been built and operated by Charles Middleton but he wanted to move out of the Kingston-Upon-Hull area due to family problems - particularly with his father in law; and so it was that Isaac went to see the property. When he returned, he was full of the place with ideas about expansion and wider distribution of the starch products. Ann was glad for him even though she knew in her heart that so many of Isaac's grand ideas she had heard before; but before anything was put into place to get him into starch production, he needed money and that was something Ann and Isaac just didn't have, however, what they did have were their families and friends.

Ann's mother came up with a hundred and fifty pounds and a hundred pounds each came from Edward Ransome and

Edward Gripper who were two of Ann's sister's husbands ; Isaac's cousin William Massey and Isaac's brother John, also advanced one hundred pounds; Isaac's sister lent him seventy pounds and another hundred came from his old friend Thomas Petchell. In total their investment was eight hundred and twenty pounds. Ann thought to herself - what a wonderful, generous and caring family they had.

It was quite firmly asserted by Isaac that all these amounts would be paid back; and indeed they were; every single penny.

*C*hapter twenty-four.

Ann and James have arrived at Pisa by train - it is now a month and a day since Isaac had been taken from her and she felt the loss acutely. He should have been here with them - sharing the beauty and magnificence all around them. All the way there, they had been in sight of The Apennines - the sun lighting up the snow-covered peaks; the valleys luxuriant with Spring crops.

But no Isaac was with her as they walked around Pisa, admiring the amazing tower structure and surrounding buildings. James was all for climbing the tower but was persuaded by Ann that it might not be the wisest thing to do.

"James - you are so much better and full of ideas for the future - which is remarkable; to climb the tower at Pisa is something that you can do another time. Just at this moment precious son of mine - I would be happier if you remained at ground level."

"Mother - you are like the mother hen when it comes to your chicks - and I will listen to your advice and forego the challenge and look up at the amazing structure; still - it would be good to stand in the place from where Galileo dropped the different sized cannon-balls."

"Yes - James but there will be time in the future for that. For now, we must concentrate on our return to Hull; and that I aim to do with you in the very best of good health"

They were seated on a bench beside the tower which gave them some shade from the sun. In many ways, Ann was a little melancholy - she certainly wanted to go home but the Williamson Street house would be very empty without Isaac at his desk or wandering round his beloved garden, which though not large by any stretch of the imagination, was still his great joy. Isaac always marvelled at the tiny seeds he planted becoming the great plants they did; his grains of mustard seed he would call them, as our Saviour had described in the parable - *becoming greater than all herbs and shooteth out great branches so that the fowls of the air might lodge under the shadow of it.*

But when they did eventually land on English soil once again - they would first make a visit to Hastings where Bessie was recovering from a severe illness almost approaching tuberculosis. It would have done her good to have been with them; she would have had the same benefits as James - but she had her family to think about and didn't want to be far from them.

Spring would not quite be over when they arrived; Ann longed to see the English bluebells and the great blossoms of the horse chestnut tree; and seeing her beloved daughter again before making the trip to Hull was very much in her heart.

As she and James sat there in the shadow of the tower of Pisa her mind went back again to their little house in Boston - in the shadow of St. Botolph's Church or "The Stump" as it was known locally; the country's biggest non-cathedral church.

They were happy days; oh yes - there were many trials and tribulations but the happiness outweighed them.

James broke her reverie.

"Shall we ever return to Menton mother?"

And thought for a moment, for indeed Menton was associated with her great sadness but certainly not the cause of it. It had been the last place she and her beloved Isaac had been together - the next time would be........... Ann gave a little shiver.

"Are you alright mother?"

Ann smiled at him.

"Yes James - I'm alright it was a little chill that came over me; shall we go back to the hotel?"

They left their seat by the tower and made their way down Via Torelli past Bagni di Nerone where it is said that the Emperor Nero liked to bathe; now in ruins but plans to excavate and restore were being debated.

Ann wondered if the emperor ever bathed in Bath; maybe he did. What a wonderful place that was - it restored Isaac just as Menton had restored James' health. She realised that she hadn't answered James question.

"Yes James - I will go back to Menton if I ever get the chance - and walk the walks I did with your father."

"Will you climb the steps up to the Basilica?"

"You never know James - I might just do that; how many are there?"

"People say different things mother but they seemed to go on for ever; could be as many as 500 twisting and turning around the hillside."

"Perhaps I won't bother then. Would you like to go back James?"

"Yes, I would - very much so. It was also the last place he and I walked together."

"You did indeed James - the last time we all walked together and a memory to treasure."

Their hotel was just off Via St. Ann - and a very grand affair - as indeed was most of Pisa - they stood by the front entrance which had a magnificent canopy - far too elaborate Ann thought but it was pleasant to sit there and that's what she decided to do.

"James - if it's alright with you - I think I might sit awhile."

"By all means mother - you said you've finished all your packing - but I've still some things to pack."

"Well you do that James and we'll meet for dinner in their magnificent dining room - for the last time."

Tomorrow they would set off for home, it would be four days before they set down on English soil; there were some railways but no junctions yet and much of the way would be by coach.

James knew that his mother's feelings were very mixed up at this very moment. Yes - he was sure she wanted to be back home in England - but on the other hand he was also aware of her uncertainty of how she would feel without his father.

It was cooler now, as Ann sat under the canopy of the hotel - a porter saw her there and brought out some iced water for her; for which she was most grateful - and said so.

Going home - she said to herself - going home; the words had a lovely ring to them. Home wasn't just a house - it was

213

family and friends - loved ones from the town and county. She would have to prepare herself for commiserations and expressions of sympathy which she would, no doubt, be greeted with. But she must be strong; she missed Isaac dreadfully but he wouldn't have wanted her to go into a decline.

She had the last memories of him relaxed and enjoying himself for a while and he was relaxed until he started wondering how his sons were doing with the business. She'd tried to tell him that everything would be going along just fine.

"Oh - Isaac Reckitt you are the stubbornest of men!" Ann chuckled to herself as those words came back to her again; but she wouldn't have had him any other way - that was her Isaac - a Lincolnshire grazier's son .... and she a Norfolk Miller's Daughter.